4 AGAINST THE MO[B]

CLEVELAND – 1935

A city terrorized by a syndicate more powerful than the Capone mob.

A city where police were on the payroll of killers, where the pay-off was as regular as the paycheck.

A city of gang murder and dead witnesses, of crime and corruption . . . until Eliot Ness and three agents moved in to make it . . .

4 AGAINST THE MOB

Oscar Fraley

CORONET BOOKS
Hodder and Stoughton

First published in Great
Britain in 1968 by
Hodder Paperbacks

Coronet Edition 1987

Although every incident is
based upon fact, certain
names, places, dates and
other details have been
altered to protect the
innocent.

Printed and bound in Great
Britain for Hodder and
Stoughton Paperbacks, a
division of Hodder and
Stoughton Ltd, Mill Road,
Dunton Green, Sevenoaks,
Kent, TN13 2YA.
(Editorial Office: 47 Bedford
Square, London WC1B 3DP)
by Hazell Watson & Viney
Limited, Member of the
BPCC Group, Aylesbury,
Bucks

British Library C.I.P.

Fraley, Oscar
  4 against the mob.
  I. Title
  813'.54[F] PS3556.R2/
  ISBN 0-340-41666-1

THE CITY OF CLEVELAND IN 1935 WAS A CESSPOOL OF CRIME.

It was overrun by mob-controlled gambling manipulated by the iron fist of a gang known as the "Mayfield Road Mob." Policy take alone was estimated at ten and a half million dollars a year and the community was paying through the nose to the tune of a hundred thousand dollars a year in "charity" rackets.

The city also was being strangled in the grip of ruthless labor racketeers, particularly in the building trades. Local business was moving out and new business absolutely refused to move in.

Bootlegging and prostitution did a land-office business. And there was no question, for those with eyes to see, that the Cleveland police department was riddled by graft and corruption. Mobsters paraded openly, betting parlors did everything but advertise in the newspapers, streetwalkers operated brazenly even in the better sections of the city, and labor racketeers openly flaunted their positions above and beyond the law. The one-way ride was almost as frequent as it had been during the worst days in Chicago and the arrogant manner in which the underworld publicly displayed its brass knuckles without police retaliation indicated plainly that political pollution and police department chicanery were hastening the disintegration of public safety.

Thus it was that, in November of 1935, the decent people of Cleveland at long last reached the end of their patience and decided the time had come for a wholesale purge. Their hope was the ballot box and they stormed this long-ignored bastion in sufficiently indignant numbers to sweep into office a pledged and determined reform ticket headed by mayoralty candidate Harold H. Burton.

As his cudgel in the monumental chore of cleaning up Cleveland, Burton chose a man named Eliot Ness.

A short time earlier Eliot Ness had become a legend in Chicago when he headed a ten-man team which had gallantly earned nationwide fame as "The Untouchables."

Dedicated and unflinching, defying threats and violence and scorning the bribe and the payoff, this fearless band had dried up Al Capone's liquid empire and also gathered much of the evidence which ultimately smashed one of the most vicious syndicates in criminal history and sent the ruthless "Scarface Al" to prison.

At the successful conclusion of the Capone case, Ness had been named the chief investigator of prohibition for the Chicago area and, after another cleanup, the government moved him to Cincinnati to bring law to the "Moonshine Mountains" of Kentucky, Tennessee and Ohio. By 1934, he was chief of the Federal Alcohol Tax Unit for the northern district of Ohio.

His fame as an incorruptible, dedicated and fearless law officer was well known to Burton. So he selected Ness as the new Public Safety Director for the city of Cleveland. Ness, only thirty-two, was the youngest man to hold the post in the city's history.

And Ness did the job. In Cleveland as in Chicago, he enlisted a hard corps of selfless allies. Unlike The Untouchables, they numbered only three—and included a lovely society girl. Also, unlike The Untouchables, the identity of these three was kept absolutely secret. Ness alone knew who they were, where they were and what they were doing. He called them "The Unknowns."

Ness and his Unknowns faced many problems, but none more challenging than that of police corruption in high—and low—places. Ness sent a number of upper-echelon police officials to prison and at one point, he cleaned out an entire precinct by way of wholesale transfers.

He swept on ruthlessly to crush the gangs and run the racketeers out of town. The underworld branded this quiet young man "The Boy Scout" when he first took over the job. But he showed them swiftly in the "Boston Club" raid, that he meant business.

Hoodlums operating this large gambling casino resisted a raid by the county prosecutor and, with machine guns jutting from the front windows, threatened to "blow off the head" of anyone who tried to enter. Ness was summoned and, unarmed because this was out of his jurisdiction, walked alone up to the front door and kicked it in.

In the days that followed, his own police tried unsuccessfully to frame him; he was threatened, shot at and physically attacked. But, as had been the case in Chicago, nothing ever was quite able to stop him.

Through six frenzied years he fought—and won—the battle of Cleveland. Ness pursued the "Mad Butcher of Kingsbury Run", the torso killer who hacked up twelve bodies and fiendishly menaced Ness and his family; routed the mobs; cleaned up the police department; changed Cleveland from the deadliest metropolis to "the safest big city in the U.S.A.", and despite all of these demanding chores still found time to establish the Cleveland Police Academy, reorganize the traffic bureau and substantially reduce juvenile delinquency by founding and directing Cleveland's Boys Town program.

Eliot Ness has become a legend in law enforcement as the result of his bestselling book *The Untouchables* and the television series of the same name which is based on his exploits.

He is pictured popularly as a grim-faced, seldom-smiling man with a mind channeled solely toward the eradication of crime and criminals. Eliot Ness *was* quiet and retiring. Yet, as a man, he was much more than a crimebuster. He had the happy faculty of being able to pack more moves into one day than most people can crowd into a week. Despite the demands on his time, he led a full home life and there he most enjoyed sprawling on the floor with the luxurious ease of a big cat while reading Shakespeare or listening to good music.

Ness had a special fondness for cats. There were times when he had as many as six of them around the house at one time.

This affection undoubtedly stemmed from their independence—much like his own—for he was a man who thrived on self-sufficiency and unhampered action. He explained it himself: "Cats don't have to be walked. You just open the door and out they go. When they're ready to come back, they come." It was this freedom, which he demanded for himself and his men, that made their movements so unpredictable to the underworld and so successful against it.

It was also typical of Ness that, in later years when the violence had gone out of police work and he went into private business, he would not have a gun in the house. Nor would he go hunting with those of his friends who enjoyed killing for sport.

"I've shot at too many men," he shrugged. "It isn't fun and I never want to kill anybody or anything again." Nor did he, as many men do, take his work home at night. Only once, according to his wife Betty, did this happen. He was highly indignant over the case of a patrolman who had taken graft but was cleared by a jury.

"There was no question but that he was guilty," he complained to his wife. "So what happened? Well, he walked into court with his wife and nine children arranged like a stepladder. Not only that, but his wife was pregnant. Everybody cried. He was acquitted.

"The thing that really sets me is that I'll swear they weren't even all his kids," Ness protested.

To this day his wife remembers this incident with amazement because it was so unusual (for him to talk shop at home.)

Eliot Ness was and has been pictured as a completely fearless man. Yet he was afraid of at least one thing—the airplane.

Still, when the occasion demanded, he was the first man aboard. His reaction is summed up best by a remark of Mark Twain's: "Courage is resistance to fear, mastery of fear—not absence of fear."

This, then, is the Cleveland story, as tense, dangerous and explosive as anything that happened to Eliot Ness during the blistering days when he and "The Untouchables" smashed the Capone empire.

Nowhere, more than in the Cleveland fight, did Eliot Ness so magnificently live out Mark Twain's definition of courage.

—OSCAR FRALEY

CHAPTER 1

MAYOR HAROLD H. BURTON, OF CLEVELAND, HAD LEFT
strict orders that he wasn't to be disturbed. The time had
come, on this cold, gray day of December 11, 1935, for
him to make one of the most important decisions of his
life.

The lettering on his outer office door was still brightly
fresh. Now he was ready to fulfill the promise which had
put it there.

He had to clean up the city of Cleveland.

One question had been uppermost in his thoughts for
months: "Who is the right man to do it?"

The minutes ticked slowly away as the mayor sat
motionless, elbows on the polished mahogany desk and
head bowed against interlaced fingers. Then, with a sud-
denness which would have startled anyone who had been
watching, his head snapped up and the palms of both
hands crashed down against the gleaming surface of the
desk.

The decision had been reached. And now impatience
rode the tall, handsome man who had been sitting there
so long and so quietly. Urgency was clear in the swift
manner in which he reached for the telephone. The long,
lean fingers drummed demandingly on the desktop through

the fleeting moments before his secretary answered. Relief was mixed with decision in his well-modulated voice as he told her:

"Get Eliot Ness, and have him come down to my office immediately."

Burton cradled the telephone, sat staring at it for a full minute and then, rising restlessly, stalked to one of the windows and stood staring out at the bleak outlines of the city of Cleveland.

One month earlier, Burton had been swept into office as the anchor man of a reform ticket which differed from most of those the city had known in the past. This one intended to keep its pledge. And now it was time for action.

A strong wind ripped in frigidly from Lake Erie, driving against the windowpanes and sending its icy breath howling around the eaves of the building. But it wasn't the weather that sent a chill creeping through the mayor.

Only now, faced at last with the imminence of action, did he fully realize the magnitude of the promise he had made and the tremendous task which lay ahead.

For Cleveland was a morass of misery and corruption. Slowly it was being strangled politically and economically by the gangster and the racketeer. Ward heelers worked hand in hand with the underworld. Underworld guns barked with all the unchecked fury of Chicago at its bloodiest, and the list of unsolved killings was a testimonial to official inefficiency. Gambling and prostitution flourished with vulgar impudence. Juvenile delinquency was reaching fearsome heights, and decent citizens were afraid to walk the streets by night. The police department, shackled by graft and corruption, had become a macabre joke. It was obvious to the most naïve that payoffs and political interference had paralyzed its efficiency, and that Cleveland had become a concrete jungle.

Burton, looking down at the crouching city, curled his

long fingers into desperate fists against the feeling of impotence which threatened to smother him. Something had to be done, quickly and decisively, to restore the morale of the city.

But who could handle such a task?

One of the first men to whom Burton's attention had been drawn in this hour of crisis was Joseph B. Keenan, an ace federal crime investigator in Washington. Keenan proved to have all the qualifications which the mayor deemed necessary for the Cleveland hot spot—that of Public Safety Director.

But the mayor was not leaping to a decision. Carefully and thoroughly he scanned his brief list of candidates. Two others who stood out were William G. Harper, head of the Cleveland office of the Federal Bureau of Investigation, and William J. McDermott, a former Assistant United States District Attorney.

The fourth man he had under consideration was Eliot Ness.

Ness, as head of his own select ten-man band of hand-chosen prohibition agents, famed as "The Untouchables," had smashed the Al Capone empire in Chicago during a bloody era of booze and bullets. Now, in Cleveland's hour of dire need, he was the chief of the Federal Alcohol Tax Unit in the northern district of Ohio with headquarters in Cleveland.

After studying the qualifications of his hand-picked candidates, Burton finally had decided Ness was his man.

He had begun to arrive at his decision earlier that same morning after making a telephone call to Keenan in Washington. Keenan himself supported Burton's own ideas on the matter.

"I think Ness would be your best bet," Keenan had told the mayor. "I happen to know that officials in Chicago think very highly of him. As a matter of fact, Dwight H. Green, who is the federal prosecutor in Chicago, says that it was Ness who actually nailed Al Capone. And from what I know, I'll go along with that."

Burton sat at his desk for almost an hour considering Keenan's recommendation. Then, leaving nothing to chance, he put in a telephone call to Green and that man, who later was to become governor of Illinois, confirmed fully what Keenan had told him.

"Do you think he could handle this job?" Burton asked.

Green chuckled.

"Handle it? Well, if he could handle the Chicago assignment I don't know what he couldn't handle. Listen, Mayor, maybe you don't realize how tough it was in Chicago."

"Well, of course, I understand it was pretty bad," Burton replied.

"Pretty bad!" Green said almost impatiently. "Capone had Chicago right in the palm of his big fat hand. He made a joke out of the law. Why, he bought 'em or he rubbed 'em out."

Green's voice gathered momentum.

"We had three thousand cops in Chicago and three hundred prohibition agents and they couldn't get even a minor conviction, let alone make a big one stick. You know why? Well, Capone is estimated to have paid off twenty-five million dollars each and every year for protection. But Ness came in here and with less than a dozen men smashed the whole damned setup. He dried up Capone and when Capone could no longer pay off, everybody went to work and started to do his job. But Ness was the man who made it possible."

Burton was enthusiastic. "That's the kind of a man I want. It sounds like he's the one."

"There's just one thing," Green interjected. "You might as well make up your mind before you talk to him that you'll have to give him a completely free hand. That's the way he worked in Chicago and you won't get him any other way. Ness is a man who won't stand for interference."

That was the clincher as far as Burton was concerned. He fully intended to keep the campaign pledge which had elected him and he knew that interference, particularly political favoritism, could be a destructive force. While sitting there at his desk, he had dissected all of the angles and now, as he awaited Ness' arrival, he breathed a sigh of relief that the decision had been made.

The mayor was still standing there, staring out over the winter-frosted façade of the city, when a ruddy-cheeked young man with a faint band of freckles across the bridge of his nose and innocent-seeming blue-gray eyes entered the mayor's outer office. He moved, almost unnoticed, through the horde of politicos, job-seekers and others waiting to see Burton, to the desk of the pretty blonde secretary. The voice was soft and yet decisive and commanding.

"Would you tell the mayor that Eliot Ness is here to see him, please?"

The secretary looked up at him and quick astonishment showed in her eyes.

So this mild-looking young man was the great Eliot Ness.

He seemed, she thought, more like a successful young business executive or a salesman in his tan camel's hair topcoat, double-breasted gray suit and maroon necktie. Yet, she had to admit to herself, there was something almost animal—pantherish?—in the way he moved that six-foot body with the broad, squared shoulders.

"Please have a seat," she told him. "I'll tell Mayor Burton that you're here."

The young man thanked her and quietly took a seat among the others who were waiting. The secretary's eyes followed him as she buzzed the mayor in his office and told him: "Mr. Ness has arrived."

Eagerness and even a faint trace of excitement were clear in the mayor's quick reply.

"Show him right in."

The secretary's voice, raised to reach Ness where he sat in a far corner with his coat folded neatly across his arm, carried through the bustling room.

"The mayor will see you immediately, Mr. Ness. You can go right in."

The rumble of conversation in the outer office was smothered by silence as every head in the room snapped up. All eyes centered on the athletic young man as he arose, crossed the room and disappeared into the mayor's inner office.

For the name Eliot Ness was widely known in the Midwest and the details of his crime-busting career had been recounted with lurid thoroughness when word had leaked out that Burton was considering him for the key office of Public Safety Director.

The curious and probing eyes followed him throughout his brief journey across the outer office until he passed into the mayor's private sanctum, where, closing the door silently behind him, he cut off the inquisitive stares. The mayor arose as he did so and advanced with outstretched hand to meet him as they inspected each other closely.

"Well, well, Mr. Ness," Burton said, "I'm really glad that I'm finally getting around to meeting you."

"It's my pleasure," Ness smiled easily. "I hope it isn't too late for congratulations on your election, Mr. Mayor."

Burton ushered him to a seat and then, without further preliminaries, went immediately to the reason for having summoned Ness to his office.

"Mr. Ness, there's no use beating around the bush. I brought you here to offer you the job of Director of Public Safety in Cleveland."

He paused, as if anticipating some sort of comment, but Ness merely nodded and waited for the mayor to continue.

"Well," Burton told him, "it wouldn't be fair if I didn't tell you first that it isn't the greatest paying job in the

16

world. And, on top of that, it has more headaches than I like to think about. But, to put it frankly, we are desperately in need of a man of your caliber."

The mayor hesitated and Ness interpected flatly: "Go on. I'm interested."

"It's only right that I tell you I've had three other men under consideration for the job. I investigated each of you fully and I chose you only after one of them recommended you."

Again Ness merely nodded.

"After all my investigation I'm convinced that you're the man for the job—if you want it."

"Tell me about it," Ness suggested.

Burton plunged into his subject; one he knew well. The tone of his voice indicated clearly the grim situation to be faced.

"This city is rotten with racketeering, graft and payoffs," the mayor said as Ness listened attentively. "When I ran for the office of mayor, I ran on a reform ticket, as you probably know, and promised that I would clean up this city. This I intend to do. And I think you are the man to help me do it.

"Your job would be to take charge of the city's twenty-four hundred men in the police and fire departments." Burton added. "I'm very much afraid that there is all too much truth to the reports of graft and corruption in the police department, otherwise progress would have been made long before now toward cleaning up the rackets. It is no secret that gambling, bootlegging and prostitution are running rampant but nothing ever seems to be done about them.

"What I want to know," the mayor asked as he sat back, folded his hands and looked steadily at Eliot Ness, "is whether you are still interested in taking on the job?"

Ness stared back at him. "It is the kind of a job I would like," he said. "But there is one thing I absolutely demand. No political interference. I must have a completely free hand."

The easy, pleasant voice had become hard and uncompromising. The mayor's tone in reply was equally determined.

"You've got it," he snapped. "This is definitely not a political appointment. I promised this city a cleanup, not a whitewash, and cleaned up it will be."

"Well," Ness asserted, "it's the only way I would consider tackling a job of this kind."

Rising from his chair, he walked over to the mayor's desk and held out his hand. They shook hands firmly.

"You've got yourself a boy." Ness grinned. "I assume I start immediately?"

Relief and eagerness were mixed in the mayor's voice. "The sooner the better."

Eliot Ness, at thirty-two, had become the youngest Director of Public Safety in the history of the city of Cleveland.

Meanwhile, outside the office word had spread throughout city hall that Ness was the man.

Wide-eyed city employees and hangers-on jammed the corridors, hoping for a glimpse of the feared gang-buster who had smashed Al Capone. Ever since the mayor first mentioned Ness, tales of "The Untouchables" had been revived by all of the newspapers in the city.

When he reappeared, quiet and boyish-looking, many of them obviously were disappointed at what they saw. He looked too unassuming, too collegiate and harmless to really have been the famous gangbuster. Most of the onlookers wrote off those legends as "a lot of newspaper talk."

Reporters were waiting for him too as he left the mayor's office.

"What are you going to do?" one newspaperman asked him.

"What's your first move?" another inquired.

Ness smiled at them in friendly fashion and shrugged his rangy shoulders.

"I have no immediate moves in mind," he told them in

that mild voice. "I want to avoid saying that I will do this or I will do that. Rather, I prefer to act first and, if there is any talking to be done, to do it afterward."

This was the way he had operated in Chicago. There, also, many of the police had been on the Capone payroll, ready to tip "Scarface Al" to any moves which Ness might disclose prematurely. Thus from the first he always had worked independently of other police with his Untouchables squad. If no one, including the police on the mob's payroll, knew when he planned to smash into a brewery or raid a night club, then no one was able to tip his hand. He had also operated in the same manner in the Cleveland area since August, 1934, as head of the Federal Alcohol Tax Unit.

During that stint he was credited with "hitting a still a day" in northern Ohio in an unswerving drive to stem the flood of illicit or untaxed whiskey. He had a reputation as a tireless agent who went out almost nightly with some of the thirty-five federal agents under his control, knocking over stills and placing hundreds of violators under federal charges.

Now he simply grinned at his inquisitors.

"I will be glad to tell you boys anything you want to know—after it has happened."

Despite Ness' reputation, the newspapers were not too optimistic as he took over his new office. But Mayor Burton, who had seen the steel beneath the velvet of the Ness manner, was certain that he had picked the right man. He said so on December 13, 1935—two days after he appointed Ness—in a speech before the Cleveland Rotary Club.

"We had a reputation that was damaging us all over the country," he told the Rotarians. "We were beginning to be tagged as a city unable to enforce the law. Now we have a man in Eliot Ness who can do what is wanted and what is needed."

During those first few days it was clearly evident around city hall that politicians, both those suspected of having certain underworld connections and those with reputable backgrounds, looked uneasily at the quiet man who had taken over as Public Safety Director. Almost unanimously they felt uncomfortable with a man who had no political affiliations and had a reputation of being beyond "reach" even for small favors. Some of the police, including the higher officials in the department, were anxious and nervous, many of them with good reason. But the reaction of one high police official summed up most of the feeling when he said: "Safety directors come and safety directors go but crooked cops go on forever."

It was a situation to dishearten even the most optimistic of men. Cleveland, like all cities of that era, was trying to fight its way out of the depression by encouraging new industry to move into the area. But the mobs, particularly those that had left the booze business, had regrouped to infiltrate gambling, vice and organized labor.

Labor racketeers exacted tribute from builders, and, rather than make a payoff, many builders refused to put their construction crews to work in the city and went elsewhere. One chain store operator who had announced that he was interested in going into Cleveland took a close look at the situation and said: "I wouldn't do it on a bet. It's too costly—and not even safe."

Eliot Ness was a man of action. And, while those in high places were sneering at him as a "Boy Scout," he served immediate notice that he would start at the top and work down in his efforts to clean up Cleveland.

His first day in office he summoned Police Chief Joseph L. Jacoby, burly and bespectacled veteran head of the Cleveland department, to his office for a showdown meeting.

Ness cut right to the heart of the matter.

"I have inspected your record and it is quite plain to me that you are a fine officer and have been doing the best you can under the circumstances."

Jacoby nodded vigorously.

"But," Ness bit off, "it is also clear that something is

wrong in this department. What we have got to do is shake it up—and I mean shake it up."

Jacoby, an expert at reading men, was not misled by the clean-cut, youthful look of the man sitting across from him.

"I can assure you," he said, "that you will have my one hundred per cent co-operation. I'll do anything that you think should be done."

There was no question, even at this first meeting, as to who was to be boss in the Cleveland cleanup.

"You will have a free rein to run your department," Ness told him. "I understand that a number of transfers and appointments have been held up during the election campaign and pending my appointment. I want you to go right ahead and make whatever appointments and transfers you think are necessary."

Ness rapped the top of his battered roll-top desk sharply with his knuckles. His voice took on a biting edge.

"There is one thing that is going to be changed around here immediately. From now on the only qualifications for promotion will be ability—not seniority. What a man does, not how long he has been here, is going to be the first consideration for advancement."

They shook hands vigorously, sealing a pact which did produce "one hundred per cent co-operation" throughout Ness's tenure in Cleveland.

But as the departing chief reached the door, Ness halted him.

"Joe," he said, "when I say I want immediate action, I mean immediate. Right now."

"You'll be hearing from me no later than tomorrow," the chief promised as he left.

As good as his word, he appeared in Ness' office the next day just at the time that Mayor Burton was lauding Ness in his Rotary Club speech.

"I've drawn a list of twenty-eight police lieutenants for immediate transfer," Jacoby told his young boss. "There are going to be a lot of raised eyebrows, because fifteen of the sixteen precincts in the city are being hit by the shifts."

"Great," Ness said. "This will show a lot of people that we mean business."

He read through the list and then looked up at Jacoby with appraising eyes.

"Go ahead. I want the department set the way you think it ought to be and responsibility fixed where it should be. Every member of this department, from the highest to the lowest, is to know what he's responsible for. That way we can check at any time and tell absolutely whether a man is doing his job."

"Okay," Jacoby agreed. "I'm with you."

Ness sat back, satisfied. It was only the beginning. But the deadbeats, those on the "take," were on notice.

CHAPTER 2

CLEVELAND WAS A HIGHLY SUSPICIOUS AND CYNICAL CITY.
It long had been accustomed to widespread graft and
corruption in high places.

Thus there were those who felt justified in sneering
at the "Boy Scout" when, just three days after his appointment, he conducted his first raid and it was described in
taunting fashion in the city's newspapers as a "fizzle."

Ness was ridiculed in the newspapers when they reported that he had accompanied police in a raid on a barbershop and come up empty-handed. The inference was
only thinly veiled that possibly the celebrated gang-buster
would find Cleveland a more difficult nut to crack than
Chicago.

"Public Safety Director Eliot Ness found a man with
earphones listening to a radio broadcast of a horse race
but there were no betting slips and no evidence that money
was being wagered," the newspapers reported.

Ness shrugged off the public indictment. Long ago he
had learned to disregard public barbs as easily as he did
private threats.

"I don't feel that I owe anybody an explanation," he
told Mayor Burton in a tight voice. "But I would like you
to know what's going on."

"I'm not asking for any explanations," the mayor said. "I know you'll handle it the way you see fit—and that it will be well done in the long run."

"Thanks," Ness said. "But just for your information, I intended to take a quiet trip around the city with the boys to observe things. Some of the reporters got wind of it, trailed me and the story hit the front pages."

The underworld laughed and so did some of the police. Ness, ignoring the criticism, wiped the smiles off their faces the very next day.

It was a startling development splashed boldly across the headlines when Ness announced the transfer of twenty-eight police lieutenants in his initial move to prepare the department for an all-out cleanup.

There was more to come, and swiftly, for a critical city that needed to learn respect for its youthful Public Safety Director.

Only two days after the first police transfers, Ness once again used the power of his new office to hit hard at police inefficiency. In a move which was completely without precedent, he summarily ordered the dismissal of two policemen who were charged with being intoxicated on duty.

Both men had previous records of having imbibed while on duty. Never, in such situations, had departmental leaders done any more than censure them.

"I will not stand for this sort of thing in my department," Ness announced.

Several high police officials warned him that he would not only be bucking civil service but also would have to contend with various political factions.

"If such is the case," Ness told Mayor Burton, "I may as well find out right now whether or not I'm going to run this department."

That night, Eliot Ness received the first of many threatening telephone calls—calls which he was to get in increasing numbers during the months and years ahead.

"Get wise to yourself, Boy Scout," a voice grated. "Put

those two guys back if you want to stay healthy." The telephone clicked dead in his ear.

But Eliot Ness remained adamant and the newspapers admitted editorially that this was "a notable departure from the policies of immediate predecessors."

"I note a particularly significant thing in the testimony concerning these men," Ness announced in standing by his dismissal order. "Other officers testified that the first thing they did when handling these men who were found to be intoxicated was to disarm them, taking away their revolvers. In London, where policemen are not armed, drunkenness on duty is sufficient cause for immediate dismissal. Here in the United States a drunken policeman is even more of a menace because he is armed.

"One of these patrolmen, assigned to school traffic duty, was entrusted with the lives of schoolchildren. Such actions cannot be tolerated, condoned or pardoned."

His voice was cold as he concluded: "It is my judgment that both of these men immediately be separated from the service."

It was a tense situation as the stony-faced Ness made the charges against them during separate hearings and demanded their immediate dismissal. For both he and the watching city knew that this was the first actual test of his authority.

One of the patrolmen had been on the Cleveland force for sixteen years. The other had been in the department for ten. The defense schemed and contrived. Schoolchildren bearing placards pleaded for their "big pals." Character witnesses lauded the patrolmen as upright men who had merely strayed and should be given another chance.

Ness cut mercilessly to the heart of the matter in hearings marked, as the newspapers put it, "by precise formality and the complete absence of the circus atmosphere in which several former public safety directors conducted hearings."

"It is this simple," Ness asserted. "Either we have a decent, law-abiding community, or we don't. Either we have decent, law-abiding policemen to show us the way, or we don't. These men have a past record of prior offenses. They don't fit."

And Ness made the dismissals stick.

There was one immediate, and heartening, result. The newspapers, finally admitting that Ness might help the situation in Cleveland, moved cautiously to support the new public safety director. The Cleveland *Plain Dealer* reported:

> The low state of police discipline and morale in Cleveland is perfectly illustrated by the fact that it was page one news when the new safety director fired two cops for being drunk on duty. It was doubly unusual because these particular cops had been in hot water three or four times before, but were still out there in the brass buttons impersonating officers.
>
> In a decently operated police department, such semimilitary disciplinary action wouldn't have been worth mentioning. It would have been customary and expected. But a quarter century of political favoritism, finagling and chiseling has left the honest cops disheartened. The ones who either stood in with the mobs or the politicians or simply did nothing got the promotions and the good jobs.
>
> The situation is not peculiar to Cleveland. It exists in practically all American city police forces. If Eliot Ness can do anything about it, his task will be as tough as Hercules' in cleaning out the Augean stables.
>
> There are still plenty of decent police in Cleveland, and they've taken heart in the last few days.
>
> A great deal of worriment has settled on the detective bureau, that ancient nest of intrigue. One political dick has been picking up suspects like nobody's business, thinking to impress the boss (previously he engaged mostly in conversation). Another, a big shot, has placed

on his desk a tome on scientific policing, in case Ness should happen around and see it. Plenty of the boys who felt secure previously have been seeing strange shadows on the wall and awakening at night with the jitters.

For years, there has been a widespread belief in the police and fire departments that it was necessary to pay $300, $500 or some such amount for an appointment or a promotion. Whether some smart guy just took the money or whether it got to the right politicians no one will ever know. Plenty of the younger and more decent cops resented it. What made them sure there was something to it was that there was no dearth of superior officers who at roll call, reading out numbers of stolen cars, would say "Q as in Cuba" or "Y as in Wyoming." They were utterly ignorant and obviously couldn't have passed an honest civil service exam.

A policeman ought to be required to pass a rigorous educational test before being appointed. A detective ought to have a thorough education. Too much attention has been paid in the past to muscle and too little to brains. Some of the police reports filed each day would horrify a fourth grade teacher. They are dumb and illiterate enough to have been prepared by movie cops.

It was clear from the tone of the story that the press still was not sure of Ness. There was that refrain . . . "if Eliot Ness can do anything about it."

Ness quickly proved that he did, indeed, intended to do something about it.

Two days later he rocked the city by announcing a total of 122 transfers—and the sensational ouster of Captain Philip K. Moss as head of the detective bureau.

Bespectacled, balding Deputy Inspector Jack Barber, nemesis of pickpockets and famed as "the man with the camera eyes," was named to succeed him. Barber had an amazing ability to place a crook at a glance. He had developed this talent in his early days as a detective by literally papering the walls of his bedroom with pictures of wanted criminals and studying them as he lay in bed.

Much was made of the fact that Moss was notable for his political activity while Barber was just as conspicuous for his avoidance of politics. It was obvious that Ness detested politicians.

Moss threatened to fight his removal on the grounds that his job had been created by the city council and none of his superiors could remove him.

Ness, however, solved the situation without too much controversy. He named Moss to head a traffic survey to reduce fatalities, one of his pet projects.

"Moss has the highest technical intelligence available in the entire department," Ness said by way of easing the switch. As it finally developed, it was a wise move; Moss laid the groundwork for a Ness drive which won for Cleveland in later years the title of "The safest big city in the U.S.A."

Yet such eventual awards were but a minor matter—as far as crime eradication was concerned—in a metropolis rated as one of the world's crookedest cities.

"I want every precinct captain to know that he is completely responsible for his district," Ness announced in a no-holds-barred edict as he ordered the first policy crackdown Cleveland had had in years.

He had thrown out the first direct challenge to the notorious Mayfield Road Mob.

Ness, a man who had learned about gangsters from the master of them all—Al Capone—knew from his operations in the northern Ohio area that Cleveland's Mayfield Road Mob was just as deadly, powerful and ruthless as the gangs that bled Chicago, New York or any other major city.

His investigations had revealed that the Cleveland Mob had been formed early in the prohibition era by Big Bill Bonelli. Big Bill was the Capone of Cleveland. He was of the old brass-knuckled school that simply would not tolerate rivals of any kind. Whenever other mobs tried to muscle in on his huge liquor syndicate they were wiped out, promptly and violently.

But just as Capone had his rivals in Bugs Moran and Dion O'Banion, Big Bill had his deadly enemies in the Manucci brothers. Open war was declared on October 19, 1927, when Big Bill and his brother Jake were lured into a trap and riddled with bullets.

Big Bill left five children, his wife, a mansion in a select section of Cleveland, one bank account of six figures in cash and a trust fund of something over a quarter of a million.

He also left his underworld empire.

And, as always, there were heirs apparent.

In the case of Big Bill's dynasty there were three: his brother, Fabian Bonelli; his eldest son, Big Augie; and his first lieutenant, Solomon (Black Sol) Valenti.

Black Sol became the boss.

But, so the grapevine said, it was a typical gangland double-cross. Black Sol, the story went, had conspired with the rival Manuccis to have Big Bill rubbed out. The underworld left nothing to the imagination. Black Sol Valenti, it reported, had been a close friend of the Bonellis when both families lived in Sicily. Working with the cunning of a Cagliostro, Black Sol had worked himself high into the Bonelli inner circle and into a position of trust with Big Bill while all the time plotting to arrange Big Bill's assassination and ultimately take over the underworld reins.

It was Black Sol, the grapevine reported, who put Big Bill and his brother Jake on the spot and had them blasted down in the barbershop of Roland Manucci.

Swiftly the whispered word reached the surviving Bonellis.

Shortly thereafter, Big Bill's widow telephoned Black Sol and asked him to meet her so they could settle a few matters. Where? Well, why not in front of the Manucci barbershop where Big Bill had been slain?

Black Sol, ignorant of the grapevine's report agreed. Anything for the wife of an old friend.

Black Sol, natty and immaculate, arrived early. After all, weren't the Manuccis his secret friends? Nothing could happen to him here. Blithely he had a shave, haircut and manicure. Then he stood in the doorway waiting for Mrs. Bonelli to arrive.

He didn't have long to wait before a large black limousine drew up to the curb and Mrs. Bonelli, still in her black widow's weeds, leaned from the window and with a friendly smile beckoned him toward the car.

With her, Black Sol saw as he stepped toward the curb, were her son, Big Augie, and her nephew, Dante Pratolini.

"Hi!" Black Sol waved as he approached the car.

The smile froze on his face as he saw the barrel of a machine gun appear over the edge of the window.

"Yeah, and good-by, you double-crossing bastard," snarled a voice from the car.

The machine gun chattered and bullet after bullet poured into Black Sol's chest. He dropped in a pool of blood, dead before his body struck the sidewalk.

Another burst of bullets poured into the lifeless body in the typical Sicilian *coup de grâce* and the limousine roared away.

There were witnesses in the barbershop who, strangely enough and in violation of the underworld code never to "sing," were willing to testify. They told graphically what had happened and the police, acting on this information, quickly arrested Mrs. Bonelli.

But Big Augie and Dante Pratolini both had vanished from the city.

The police also jailed Alberto Ruffia, who, in the peculiarly intermingled factions of the Cleveland underworld, was related to both the Bonellis and the Valentis. And a short time later they took into custody one Mike Silvero, holding both of them as eyewitnesses to the killing.

Feeling that there was a strong case, the county grand jury speedily indicted the widow and the two fugitives on first degree murder charges.

Actually, Mrs. Bonelli was being held to induce her son and nephew to return and give themselves up. But they remained fugitives and eventually the widow was brought to trial. Numerous alibis were produced, and she won a quick acquittal.

But the blood bath had not ended.

In reprisal for Black Sol's slaying, the remaining Bonelli brother, Fabian, was gunned down as he played cards peacefully in a cigar shop. It was the old familiar story. A curtained black limousine slid smoothly up to the curb, a machine gun poked into view and a hail of bullets snuffed out the life of the unsuspecting victim.

Except for the acquitted widow, that slaying erased the last of the senior Bonellis. And with Big Augie and his cousin Dante Pratolini both fugitives from justice, the Manuccis took over complete and undisputed power of the Cleveland underworld.

Their reign was short-lived.

Once Big Bill's widow was acquitted, and freed of trial jeopardy, both Big Augie and Dante reappeared in Cleveland. The police didn't have to go looking for them. They both gave themselves up voluntarily, and each showed a cheerful disregard for the charges.

The reason soon became evident.

When they were brought to trial it was quickly discovered that Alberto Ruffia, the state's star witness, wisely had slipped out of the country. An intensive police hunt disclosed that he had returned to Italy and he successfully fought all efforts to have him returned.

Big Augie and his cousin Dante boasted that they had the rap beaten. But they screamed threats of vengeance, when Mike Silvero's testimony convinced a wide-eyed but unintimidated jury of their guilt.

Valenti had been the thirty-eighth victim in the long and deadly struggle for mob power in Cleveland. The

31

surprise verdict against Big Augie and his cousin was the first conviction the state had been able to muster in any one of those thirty-eight violent deaths—and the courtroom became a mob scene when the verdict was announced and the two pasty-faced defendants were sentenced to life imprisonment.

"You'll pay for this," Big Augie glared at Silvero.

Mrs. Bonelli burst through the gate from the spectators' seats and rushed at the jury box, screaming and waving her fists in the faces of the frightened jurors. Then, turning her back on them, she panted to the bar and there shouted threats into the face of the judge.

White-faced, the judge pounded for order and shouted at a bailiff: "Get this woman out of here. I want some order in the court."

Mrs. Bonelli continued screaming until she was forcibly removed from the courtroom while a squad of deputies forced their way to the side of the defendants, shackled them and led them off to a cell.

Meanwhile, other members of the Bonelli clan joined the clamor, screaming and shouting, until police finally had to be called to clear the courtroom and disperse the crowds which had gathered outside. But growling bands of Sicilians congregated on nearby corners, talking excitedly and glowering in the direction of the courtroom, while the understandably fearful jurors stayed inside.

To avoid any violence or further demonstrations the court ordered the jurors escorted to their homes under police guard. They were spirited out of a rear door and whisked away in police cars.

But the trial was not yet over. To Cleveland's sorrow, hulking, sallow-faced Big Augie, as well as his cousin Dante, were not destined to serve out that life sentence.

The defense lost the first round but it had plotted well. On the grounds of error in the record and numerous other legal technicalities, the convictions were set aside in the court of appeals and new trials were ordered.

Now the defense had a real ace.

The first time Ruffia had been conveniently absent in Italy. This time, Silvero, the state's chief witness in obtaining the convictions, also had decided that the climate was much more healthy in the old country. He too had vanished and when located in Sicily was also able to successfully fight extradition.

The state was left without a single witness. The facts were obvious to all and yet, without witnesses or corroborated evidence, the court had no recourse but to acquit both of the sneering defendants.

And, once Big Augie and his cousins Dante were free, retribution came swiftly to the Manuccis.

The executioners worked systematically. The head of the clan, John Manucci, was the first to be assassinated—just as Big Bill Bonelli was the first of his family to perish in a hail of bullets. Manucci and his chief bodyguard, Tony Angelo, were mowed down in a barrage which made a shambles of the Italian restaurant where they were dining.

Their slayings were never solved, chiefly because the witnesses who were on the premises swore that they had seen "absolutely nothing."

The next man to be put on the spot was Valentine Joseph Manucci, the Number Two man in the family. Just three weeks after the death of his brother John he was taken for a one-way ride—his bullet-riddled body discovered in a ditch with the precautionary bullet hole squarely between the eyes.

The underworld was jumpy. Investigating police were given a wide berth. The most valuable stoolies clamped their lips together and hid out. This, said the grapevine, was only the beginning. And the grapevine was terribly right.

For next came Cleveland's own "Little St. Valentine's Day Massacre."

Five of the Manuccis had gathered at a certain street corner—later to be known as the "Bloody Corner"—in answer to telephoned messages.

33

"What's this all about?" demanded Roland Manucci.

The four men with him all looked puzzled.

"Damned if I know," said his brother Raphael. "I got your message to meet you here."

"Me, too," chimed another.

"I didn't send you guys no damned messages," the swarthy Roland barked. "Who the hell are you kiddin'?"

"Honest to God." Raphael frowned. "I get a telephoned message which says you want to meet us all here."

"It's a damned phony," Roland growled as the others confirmed Raphael's story as the same thing that had happened to each of them. "I got a message too that you want me to meet you here. We better get t'hell outta here."

But it was too late.

The inevitable black limousine roared down the street toward them, tires squealed as it pulled to the curb and guns roared.

Roland no more than reached for the gun in his shoulder holster when the bullets slammed him to the sidewalk. It was the same with the others. They never had a chance against the leaden stream of death.

When the thunder of the barrage died away, Roland lay dead on the sidewalk. Dead, too, were his brother Raphael and a Manucci lieutenant, Giuseppe Verdi. The two other members of the Manucci faction were severely wounded and both subsequently fled from the city.

Protesting his innocence, Big Augie Bonelli once more was arrested in the frantic police investigation that followed the bloody massacre. Nothing could be pinned on him and he was set free.

That fusillade at the "Bloody Corner" marked the end to the Bonelli-Manucci feud.

The Manuccis had been wiped out completely and the Mayfield Road Mob was in complete control.

For a quiet but fat and lucrative period, the gang rode

along high, wide and unbothered. Nobody else had the muscle to move in. The organization was too powerful. And there was another reason.

By this time, boundary lines had been drawn sharply in every section of the nation. The submachine gun and the sawed-off shotgun had weeded out the brash and the greedy. Organization meetings had been held among the top mobsters and territorial lines had been sharply defined. Shrewd brains in the top echelon of the Mafia had come to the conclusion that continued violence and killing could produce only one eventual result: the rising protests of decent, law-abiding citizens which would force an all-out cleanup.

It was simply a matter of self-preservation that dictated getting their criminal house in order.

But just as crime on a national basis was falling into a loose but effective alignment, the lush and lucrative racket of catering to illegal thirsts died along with the demise of prohibition. Bootlegging had been a golden bonanza. Now other sources of revenue would have to be found.

It happened in New York. It was the same in Chicago. And things were no different for the mobsters of Cleveland.

So, when prohibition passed out with the year 1933, the Mayfield Road gang found it necessary to turn to other lucrative if illegal methods of turning a quick buck. The mob grabbed the big gambling casinos, took a steely grip on vice, controlled the slot machine racket and backed the bookie joints, while retaining the reduced but still profitable income from illicit whiskey.

It soon discovered, however, that it was missing the biggest gravy train of them all. This was the policy and clearing house racket—known more familiarly as the "numbers game."

When the mob began to move in, the numbers game was almost completely in the hands of relatively harmless operators headed by a group called the "Big Four." This group was composed of Reuben (The King) Jacobs, Fred D. Murphy, Georgie Anderson and Horace Mann.

This quartet soon was stripped of its power. Jacobs died. Murphy was shot. Anderson and Mann took the hint and turned stooges for the mob. Murphy, after he recovered from his wounds, did likewise. Scores of other minor operators fled from the racket, signed up with the muscle men or were murdered.

Once again it was a time of terror.

With methodical precision the other operators either fell into line and took their orders from the mob or they were rubbed out.

Alex B. Connelley, once a powerful figure in a policy whose volume of business was exceeded only by that of the "Big Four," boasted openly that he would not pay tribute to the new self-appointed overlords. His stubbornness brought its reward. One night, shortly after he had scorned a final ultimatum, he drove up to the garage beside his home and opened the door to step out. As he did, two figures emerged from the shubbery and emptied their pistols into him. He was found slumped over in the front seat of his automobile—dead.

An operator named Frank Morelli could not, and would not, understand why he should share his fine annual income with what he described as "punk blackmailers." One evening as he entered his automobile in downtown Cleveland, two men pushed their way in behind him. Morelli, with a gun pressing into his ribs, was ordered to drive to a lonely spot near the railroad. His bullet-torn body was found there the next day.

Gordon McManus, a big-time independent operator who also insisted on keeping his profits all for himself, boasted that he had friends in the mob. He did. So they were particularly patient with him. Twice he was taken for near rides, told what would happen to him if he didn't get smart, and then allowed to go free on the promise that henceforth he listen to reason. McManus ignored these friendly suggestions.

When he was found in an automobile in a suburb of Cleveland, there was a pound of lead in his body.

John McPhail, another hard-headed operator, defied instructions to get in line. He was riding along the street in his automobile when another machine pulled up alongside him. The tommy gun chattered in his face and McPhail was pronounced dead on arrival.

Recalcitrant Bobbie Gillens was snatched off a sidewalk, pumped full of bullets and then pushed out into a gutter.

"Careful" Johnson, another stubborn operator, unfortunately did not live up to his nickname. He, too, was driving along by himself when another automobile drew up beside him. There was the familiar staccato sound of death from the machine gun wielded by one of the mob's experts—and another unsolved murder to baffle the harried police.

There were many, many more.

Philip Gunn, another of those who refused to step into line, was standing in a confectionery store downtown when two men walked up beside him and shot him dead. In true Mafia style, one even took time to bend over, place his pistol at the dead Gunn's forehead, and fire the ceremonial make-sure shot.

Andy Barton, who once served as a bodyguard and lieutenant for the "Big Four," was lucky. He spotted his would-be slayers and there was a running gun battle in the streets. Barton had an arm shot off but did escape with his life.

The Mayfield Road Mob stopped at nothing. Ruthlessly they backed up their demands with sawed-off shotguns, machine guns and "muscle," a designation for their mauling, blackjack-wielding thugs.

Practically every operator in Cleveland soon was whipped into line or exterminated. It was much like the early days of prohibition when gangland guns barked almost daily in a never-ending battle over the right to operate the territory. There was one difference. This time the mob was doing the attacking and the exterminating without any strong fear of reprisal.

Dutch Schultz in the days of his greatest affluence and influence never enjoyed a policy setup comparable to the one perfected by the Mob in Cleveland. The New York gangster was content with a system which insured his mob the bulk of the daily lottery investments. In short, Schultz had to take the bad with the good, for there were some losing days along with the winning ones.

In Cleveland there were no losing days for the gang that mercilessly stamped out the independents who refused to pay tribute. It devised a foolproof, profit-every-day system. The Mayfield Road Mob simply by-passed the losing days by "renting" the policy franchises to individual operators. Under this system, the individual operators took the risk but the mob took the cream of the profits.

As it was run, a single operator might lose as much as five to ten thousand dollars on any single day if a certain heavily played number happened to hit. But this was of no concern to the mob.

The operators paid an allotted sum for the franchises. They also were forced to pay a stipulated amount each week for the "protected" privilege of being allowed to operate. This payment had to be made, win or lose. The mob was not interested in the financial condition of those it allowed to stay in business. It accepted no alibis and no excuses. As an example, the larger houses paid as much as forty per cent of their gross business. And this payoff had to be made whether they realized a profit or suffered a loss at the week's end.

It was sudden death for the operator, large or small, who came up short.

Eliot Ness had more than an inkling of this situation when he took over as Public Safety Director. Yet even Ness was surprised at the volume of business and the staggering amounts of money involved.

"I thought I knew pretty well what was going on around here because I have been in this area quite some time now," he told his top-echelon police officials at a special meeting. "I'm sure that most of you must know something about it too. But what I have discovered already is little short of amazing and," a hard note crept into his voice, "I don't see how it could have completely escaped the notice of officers who should have known. But the time has come when we are going to close down these policy racketeers —and I mean completely."

The next night—less than one month after he took office —he led a raid on a policy drawing and took 150 men into custody.

"This is only a beginning, I know," Ness admitted. "But it is something."

It also served notice that things were about to be broken wide open in the long-corrupt city of Cleveland.

But Bob Turley, a local cartoonist, remained skeptical. He sent Ness a poem which read:

> Says Ness, to every City "Cop,"
> "This gambling business has to stop!
> These slot machines are running wild,
> They steal the nickels off a child.
> They steal from men and women too,
> On them, I now put my taboo.
> No one can beat a gambler's game;
> Show me the man, or name his name?
> Bring in machines, sweep city clean,
> You hear me say just what I mean.
> Do your duty; have no fear,
> Not as long as Ness is here."
> But will they do it, now I ask,
> Or will "Coppers" shirk the task?

Will they tip things off before,
Then walk boldly to the door?
You can't tell what "Cops" will do,
Hate to say it, but it's true.

Ness got the message, not the joke.

CHAPTER 3

ELIOT NESS UNDERSTOOD FROM THE BEGINNING THAT HE needed the right tools for the job at hand—an "Untouchable" police department—if he hoped to get to the Mob and clean up the city of Cleveland.

During his term with the Federal Alcohol Tax Unit, he had spent enough time in the vicinity of Cleveland to have strong suspicions that many of the rumors about crooked cops on the force must be true. He knew, definitely, that a number of them had been "touchable" during the prohibition era; it was a fact that certain officers had given protection to bootleggers.

And, he deduced shrewdly, a policeman who was on the "take" during the booze era quite likely would still be accepting bribes and payoffs in vice, gambling and perhaps even the labor racketeering to which the mobs turned after prohibition died.

His first major break came in 1936 through the combined efforts of an immigrant who had been a soldier-hero for his adopted country and an enterprising reporter from the Cleveland *Press*.

The opportunity presented itself in the person of Chris Gutman, a bald, middle-aged immigrant laborer. Chris, a hulking, good-natured man, had saved two thousand dollars from his meager wages after returning from France, where he had been wounded and gassed as a doughboy in the American Army. The bad days of the depression had melted Chris' life savings by one-half. Then, to make matters worse, a high-pressure racketeering sales force invaded Chris' neighborhood.

"The Building and Loan Association where you have your savings is so shaky that it can go under at any time," a slick-talking, greasy-haired salesman told him glibly. "Chris, believe me, I can double your money in sixty days."

Chris parted with a thousand dollars of his hard-earned savings and was given some "security bonds" which, it later developed, actually were deeds to forty cemetery lots.

When the sixty days passed, the optimistic Gutman jubilantly went to the cemetery company for his "doubled money." Chris was told to "come back later." In succeeding days, the directions always were the same and the suspicion that he had lost his money grew in Chris' mind.

The cemetery lot racket in reality was a scheme by which fast-talking salesmen unloaded otherwise worthless real state at high prices to unsuspecting victims. One six thousand dollar pasture had been boosted to a six million dollar profit by these hustlers.

Finally it became obvious to Chris that he had been swindled.

"Someday," the irate Gutman bitterly promised one of the cemetery company employees, "you people are going to wish that you had the sense to pay me."

In great indignation, Gutman went immediately to the Better Business Bureau, but they were unable to help him. Then he went to the county prosecutor and once again it was the same futile story. Finally, in desperation, he hired a lawyer, only to learn that there apparently was nothing he could do about the broken promises. So, as a last resort, Gutman went rather forlornly to the offices of the Cleveland *Press* and ultimately was handed over to a reporter named Carl Swanson.

Swanson was the perfect example of a newspaperman with a keen "nose for news." A wiry man in his thirties, who usually wore a bow tie, he had joined the Scripps-Howard paper in Cleveland a year earlier. Swanson, after listening closely, scented a story.

First he explored Gutman's story in great detail. Then he went with Gutman and together they dug up scores of victims of the cemetery lot racket. Swanson, who frequently had accompanied Ness on his raids and scouting expeditions, finally turned his information over to the Public Safety Director and Ness, in turn, handed it over to the grand jury. The panel returned indictments which cracked the cemetery lot racket wide open.

Swanson, seeking a follow-up angle, because of his aid in breaking the case was given access to the books of one of the cemetery companies which was involved, and in them he discovered the name of one "T. L. Radek." This name was on the books for the astonishing total of nearly a hundred thousand dollars' worth of graveyard real estate. The telephone directories listed but few Radeks and Swanson's dogged investigation showed that none of them seemingly were in a position to purchase lots in such a large quantity.

Yet, something about the name intrigued this inquisitive newspaperman. Swanson mulled over the name, twisting the letters around and around for hours until, suddenly, the letters fell into place. For his repeated transpositions finally spelled out the name "Drake."

And Theodore L. Drake was a captain in the police department.

Excitedly, Swanson went to Eliot Ness and told him of his hunch.

"Eliot," he insisted, "I really think I have something here."

Ness stared at the name "Radek" with narrowed eyes

which widened as Swanson rearranged the letters to spell "Drake."

"Yes," Ness agreed, "maybe you do have something."

Ness hurried to Prosecutor John Matthews with Swanson's information and they went to work immediately, digging meticulously into Police Captain Theodore L. Drake's financial condition. They stared at each other in disbelief when investigation disclosed that Drake had sums totaling over a hundred thousand dollars on deposit in various banks. Much of the amount had, it was learned, been piled up in the 1921–1931 period while he was operating as a supposed protector of law and order in precincts where a vast percentage of Cleveland's trade in booze, babes and betting existed.

It was never to be fully explained why Drake, a tall powerful man with a protruding stomach, had so much money tied up in the cemetery lots. Investigation showed, however, that he had invested nearly a hundred thousand in Laurel Valley Cemetery lots under the name of Radek. There were two general theories: that the lot salesmen had "held him up" when they discovered he had great amounts of unexplained money, or that he might have been involved in the racket himself. Neither of these theories ever was proved. Some believed that he was a genuine victim of the swindle.

"But what I really want to know," Ness fumed, "is how an honest cop could get his hands on that kind of money."

All told, it was discovered that Drake had the hundred thousand in cash salted away in four different banks and that he had used four different names at various times on these accounts.

"I didn't want to be embarrassed by people asking me for loans," he shrugged in explanation.

But despite this affluence, the round-faced police captain with the bald, gray-fringed head, was content to live in a modest, unpainted house which was appropriate to his $3,500-a-year police pay.

44

"Drake has been on the force thirty years and in that time he has received a total salary of $67,966," Ness figured. "Where did he get the hundred thousand?"

Ness turned loose his bloodhounds and the web soon was spun tight around the quiet, smiling man of simple tastes who often spent Sunday afternoons during the summertime at Laurel Valley Cemetery listening to organ music. Close scrutiny of his activities revealed that Drake once had been general manager of the Locksmith Manufacturing Company, an ill-fated firm which had lost money in an attempt to market a combination-type lock for automobiles. His money, it was shown, certainly had not come from that venture.

"The reputation of the whole department is at stake," Ness told Mayor Burton. "This is the first concrete example we have had of police corruption and I am personally taking charge of this investigation."

Carefully, Ness made a list of the known bootleggers who had operated in Cleveland through the 1921–1931 era. Then the young Safety Director set out to see as many of them as he could. It was an exhaustive inquiry which led him into grimy basement apartments, down gloomy alleys to dirty hole-in-the-wall rooms and to sedate homes in the suburbs where the most successful bootleggers had retired.

It was a demanding task which required plodding patience, bulldog determination and tactful persuasion before the Drake story unfolded completely.

"He was one of the boys I had to pay off," said a wheezing little man sitting in a tattered overstuffed chair in a dingy tenement room. "They bled us white."

"He told me right out that I had to pay up or go to jail," said another near-vagrant with obvious bitterness. "So I paid up. What else could I do?"

The case against Drake built rapidly. Two others swore to Ness that the captain had accepted two new automobiles as well as cash. Doggedly the young crime-buster correlated his information, and no less than thirty

45

prohibition era violators ultimately agreed to testify in court that they had paid off to the police captain.

"It's all there," Ness told Mayor Burton wearily. "I've got it, chapter and verse, and I've got the witnesses to back it up. Maybe it's a black eye for the department, but we've got to wash our own linen before we can get the city's respect."

When the case was presented to the grand jury, one witness, identified as a former speakeasy operator named Ned Marvick, blew off gustily to reporters.

"I used to buy a lot of 'clambake' tickets from the police," he said. "The cops who collected told me that the 'clambakes' were for Captain Drake.

"That wasn't all, either," he added. "The collector also came around every Christmas and collected fifteen or twenty bucks 'for the boys.' On top of this I was paying way above the market price for hard liquor. But what could I do? I understood the money was going to police protection."

Drake ultimately was indicted on charges that he solicited a new automobile on December 24th, 1924, from Peter Metzinski and Herbert Lebedovski; another new automobile from the same pair on June 9, 1927; a considerable sum in cash from Matzinski on December 24, 1924; a much larger amount from Lebedovski between 1926 and 1931; and still more from Metzinski between 1928 and 1931.

"Bribes were paid to influence him with respect to his official duties as police captain in the enforcement of the laws of the State of Ohio particularly relating to the possession, manufacture and sales of intoxicating liquors," the indictment charged.

Ness pressed for immediate trial so that the case would serve as a lesson to other evildoers or potential wrongdoers on the force. Justice then moved into high gear. Drake was tried and convicted on five counts of bribery during the prohibition era and on May 26, 1936, was sen-

46

tenced to a two-to-twenty-year-term in the Ohio State Penitentiary.

One year later, the United States Supreme Court rejected Drake's appeal and he was led off to prison.

Eliot Ness was not happy. He was, rather dismayed that a sharp reporter—and not one of the investigators in his own department—had ferreted out this ugly skeleton in the police department closet.

"There is only one thing to do." His voice was grim. "I'm going to have to go back to the old Chicago formula that made 'The Untouchables' so successful."

He slammed closed the cover of his neatly ordered roll-top desk with a decisive crash, startling the county prosecutor, John Matthews.

"John, I'm going to have to bring in outsiders who will be free to investigate without being smothered by old alliances or checked at every turn because they are too well known."

"That's up to you," the prosecutor replied.

Thus did Ness begin the formation of a private staff of investigators who were to be characterized as: "The Unknowns."

Up to this time, Ness ordinarily lunched quietly in his favorite haunt, the Bronze Room of the Cleveland Hotel, with an ever-changing group which to all appearances was composed principally of casual friends. Some of these eating companions actually were undercover men.

This chameleon group included G-Men who were "co-operating" with Ness, particularly on out-of-town assignments. Still others were members of his personal staff or police rookies not familiar to the racketeers. But the Drake case convinced him that absolutely anonymous outsiders would have to be brought in to do a thorough surgical job on his own department.

"The Unknowns" were to be his answer.

47

ELIOT NESS KNEW THAT WHAT HE NEEDED MOST TO clean up the crooked elements in his police department were not "shake-ups." The only sure-fire method was "shake-outs"—getting rid of the tainted cops and jailing them if it was possible.

But the Drake case had proved to him that he could no longer continue to handle all of the investigating work himself. He mulled the matter over in his mind and then went to see Mayor Burton with a plan.

"I've got to have the funds for outside assistance," he told the mayor. "I want to put on some special operatives and I need special funds to pay for them if we're going to get the job done.

"It isn't that the men we have can't or won't do the work I have in mind," he added. "Nor is it that I don't trust some of the men I could name to you. But there are such things as loyalties and sympathies and I want strangers who won't be swayed in any manner. I can't do it all myself and I've got to have this assistance."

Burton agreed almost immediately.

"I told you when I gave you this job that I wanted it done and that I'd do anything in my power to help you," he told Ness. "I'll see just how large a budget I can get for you and we'll mark it for 'special services.' You can handle it as you like."

Ness was jubilant. He had the green light to form his own inside detail which was to be heralded as "The Unknowns."

"All I need is a couple of good men I know I can trust," he advised the mayor. "Whatever it costs us, you can bet that we'll be getting more than our money's worth."

"I'll leave that to you," Burton said in parting. "I like the way things have been shaping up."

Returning to his own office, Ness analytically considered the names of completely ethical and capable men he knew in other areas. It was the same routine he had followed when, given the Capone assignment in Chicago, he had "drafted" agents from other areas. The problem was much the same this time. He wanted men who not only would be unknown to the Cleveland hoods but, of equal importance, also would be alien to his own police.

After long deliberation, Ness selected two men whom he knew to be completely trustworthy, able and courageous.

One of these men was Barney Davis, with whom Ness previously had worked in the Federal Alcohol Tax Unit. Davis would be perfect, he pondered, for the "shadow" work that lay ahead.

Barney was a small, blond man with a face virtually impossible to pick out in a crowd. He seemed to melt into almost any background and Ness was well aware of his ability as a top-flight "tail." He also rated the little man highly for his bravery and honesty.

Several telephone calls produced the information that Barney was in Philadelphia and Ness put in a call to him there. When he finally got Barney on the phone they exchanged pleasantries and then Ness could almost see the smile on Barney's face as he asked: "What's on your mind, Eliot?"

"Well," Ness replied, "I wondered whether you could join me here in Cleveland and give me a hand in a job I'm trying to do?"

"I've heard here and there what you're doing," Barney said. "It might be downright interesting. The way I get it, you might see a little trouble."

"Could be," Ness said. "Are you interested in coming here?"

"Will tomorrow be soon enough?" Barney Davis inquired dryly.

Ness chuckled appreciatively.

"That be fine, Barney, and I think I can promise you some fun."

The other man in whom he was interested had been one of his most valued operatives during the deadly days in Chicago. This was Jim Manski, one of the "Untouchables" who had helped him smash the Capone mob in Chicago. Manski was an ex-Army officer who flew his own plane "just for the excitement and the hell of it." The sandy-haired six-footer was a crack shot and a wire-tap expert as well.

Always, when he thought of the imperturbable Manski, Ness remembered a tense night in a dark alley behind the Montmartre Café in Chicago. This was the Capone headquarters and the "Untouchables" needed a wire tap on the place.

Through a ruse, the Capone guards had been lured away momentarily. At this point, Manski calmly climbed the telephone pole at the rear of the café and tapped the terminal box. Had the guards returned before he finished, Manski, dangling at the top of the pole, would have been a sitting duck.

Ness had stood at the base of the pole that night with pistol in hand, and he confessed later that "every minute Jim was up that pole seemed like a year to me." They had managed to get the job done and get away before the guards returned and the information obtained through that wire tap had played a major role in smashing the Capone syndicate.

Ness' mind relived those nerve-chilling moments as he tracked down Manski by telephone and finally located him in California, where Manski just was finishing up another job in his long career as a dedicated law officer.

"It's good to hear from you, chief," Manski said. "What's cooking?"

"Plenty," Ness told him, rapidly giving Manski a fill-in on the situation in Cleveland. "I called because I could use you here for some undercover work. I don't know how long it will take but it should be right up your alley."

Manski laughed at Eliot's unintentional pun.

"You have some more telephone poles you want climbed?"

"You never know," Ness laughed. Then he asked, "How about it, Jim?"

"I'm just finishing up here," Manski said. "I can be there next Monday."

"Fine," Ness told him with relief. "I'll be looking forward to seeing you."

That same weekend, at a small dinner party at his home, Ness added a third member to his "Unknowns" who would have been a distinct surprise to almost anyone contemplating a gangbusting operation.

It was a woman.

And a beautiful one. Her name was Virginia Allen and she was a tall, stately blonde who was well known in Cleveland society circles as an excellent trapshooter and all-round sportswoman.

They were discussing sports, for Ness was an avid tennis player, and the conversation got around to psychological reactions when going for victory or in fighting off a defeat.

"I don't know why it is," Virginia told him, "but I always seem to be more calm and composed when I know I have to beat off a set point or when I have to sink a putt to win. It's peculiar, but my whole life seems to be this way. Once I narrowly escaped a frightful automobile collision. Instead of being shaken up, I was the calmest person on the scene."

"You'd make a good agent," Ness smiled. "We need people with that kind of reaction."

"It would interest me," she said soberly, "if I were a man."

Ness leaned forward, suddenly serious, as a thought struck him.

"Listen, Virginia, how would you like to work for me as an undercover agent?"

"You must be kidding," she said.

"No," Ness replied, the tone of his voice convincing her that he was serious. "I honestly do mean it. Look at it this way. Nobody would be suspicious of one of our society leaders if she decided to take a fling in some of the gambling clubs."

Virginia nodded. "I suppose not."

Ness smiled slowly at her, his eyes speculative.

"You know, underneath all that peaches and cream I have an idea that you've got a lot of nerve and you could take care of yourself. Besides, I'd do my best to see that you never got into any real bad spots without having help available. What do you say to the idea?"

"Well, I'd say that I'd probably be scared to death," she admitted candidly. "But, Eliot, it would be interesting and, you know, it might give some real meaning to my life." She paused, frowning for a minute, then made up her mind. "All right. I'll do it."

"Good," Ness said softly.

And thus were the "Unknowns" formed.

Ness gathered them together the next week, issued them credentials and then gave them a complete fill in on how the Mayfield Road Mob controlled the underworld of Cleveland; how the bookies and policy operators rented their individual franchises for "protection"—

protection from the mob's muscle—and his suspicions that a number of high police officials were "on the take."

Manski was instructed to set up immediately in certain suspect precinct houses an elaborate system of wire taps to record suspicious conversations which might reveal wholesale graft in the police department. Ness arranged to borrow wire-tap equipment from federal agencies, including "Pam-O-Graph," which could be attached to suspected telephone lines and record conversations.

"I want you to monitor the calls to all of my top men," Ness told his valued assistant from the old days in Chicago. "I hate to do this. Somehow it seems a little on the sneaky side. But it just has to be done until we can separate the good from the bad."

"Well, it worked before." Manski shrugged, and set about making the necessary arrangements.

Next, Eliot Ness called in his other two Unknowns, Barney Davis and Virginia Allen, and briefed them on his suspicions regarding one of his senior police officers, Captain Lewis E. Howland.

The Howland matter, Ness explained, had come to his attention on June 1, 1936, when Councilman Owen Mihailich became involved in a dispute with the captain, who was in charge of the precinct that included Mihailich's ward.

A wire fence had been erected to keep bathers from using Lake Erie along a certain stretch of waterfront. Mihailich insisted staunchly that this was a public area and that no one had a right to fence it off. Taking a pair of wire cutters, he went out in the early morning hours and snipped away the barrier.

Howland was infuriated because he had ordered the fence erected in the first place.

"If Mihailich was the one who cut that wire, I'll put him in jail," he raged.

As a matter of fact, nothing at all was done about Mihailich's act—a curious thing in itself.

But it was the last straw for Mihailich, who had been battling Howland for years over the unrestrained vice in his ward. He went storming to Ness with what he knew about gambling and vice in Howland's bailiwick.

Now, Ness felt, was the time to move on the Howland situation, and he gave sharp-eyed Davis and the lovely Virginia crisp instructions.

"I've issued orders to the captains of every district to tighten up all over town during the tourist and convention season," Ness added. "I want you two to move around Howland's district, keep your eyes and ears open, and see what you can find out. If there's gambling going on there, I want to know about it."

"We'll find it, if it's there," Barney said.

"I know that," Ness smiled. "And, Barney, I'll leave it up to you to watch out for Virginia if there's any trouble."

"I think," Barney said with a slow grin, "that Virginia can take good care of herself. But you can bet I'll be there if she needs any help."

Before the week was out, Ness' strategy was to pay off. Mihailich stormed into his office again and protested that gambling was operating "high, wide and profitable" at the White Swan Night Club, right in the heart of Captain Howland's district. Mihailich made his visit on a Thursday afternoon.

"Something has to be done about this," the councilman thundered after making his charges.

"It will be, Councilman," Ness told him. "I should have a full report by this time tomorrow because I've been making an investigation of my own."

Mihailich snorted indignantly.

"Investigations! This calls for action, not investigations."

Ness turned stern.

"Listen, Councilman, I'll do this job my way. To be perfectly frank, I know that you've had trouble with Howland. Now, just because he's one of my men, it

54

doesn't mean I'm backing him if he's wrong. But I personally am going to know he's wrong before I make a move which might jeopardize a man with his years of service in what could—mind you I say 'could'—be just a personal vendetta. As I told you, be here tomorrow and you'll have my decision."

Mihailich departed, unconvinced.

Ness ignored the councilman's chagrin. He wasn't telling Mihailich, or anybody else, about his "Unknowns." But he did summon Barney Davis and Virginia Allen to appear in his office the next morning. When they arrived, he came right to the point.

"Well, what have you been able to find out?"

Barney and Virginia hadn't lost any time. Pretending to be two friends out for a good time, they had combed Howland's district.

"There's one hot spot," Barney reported. "That's the White Swan Night Club. It seems to be a swinging operation and I'd have to bet, Eliot, that it's getting protection from the department. It runs so openly that it couldn't operate otherwise."

"Mihailich was right then," Ness snapped. "Okay, you two keep looking around and keep me advised what you come up with. Meanwhile, I'll take care of the White Swan."

Later that day, when Mihailich appeared as scheduled, Ness surprised the suspicious councilman by saying: "You seem to be right about Howland. My investigation shows that gambling is running wide open at the White Swan. We'll raid it tomorrow and I'd like you to come along just to witness how we operate."

"It seems that I had you wrong," Mihailich admitted. "I thought maybe you'd try to cover up for one of your men."

"I," Ness retorted grimly, "cover up for no one."

Ness laid his plans carefully so that there would be no "leak." He ordered a squad car and several of his best men to be on hand late the next afternoon, a balmy Saturday in early June, and no one but he and Mihailich knew where they were going until they had left Central Police Headquarters.

When they were a block from the White Swan, Ness ordered the car stopped and sent two men to approach from the rear. Then, when those men were in position, Ness and the councilman, accompanied by another officer, swarmed up to the front of the gambling joint.

Ness didn't bother to knock. He simply raised one foot and kicked in the door with a solid smash of his heel. Sixteen persons in the big front room were listening to the call of a horse race and they simply stared open-mouthed as Ness, Mihailich and the patrolman rushed inside just as the two other officers appeared from the rear.

"Okay, just take it easy and nobody will get hurt," Ness said. "This is a police raid."

One woman screamed and fainted. A man began to curse savagely over the sound of the race caller and Ness yelled: "Knock that thing off and everybody keep quiet."

At this moment, a square-shouldered young man appeared from upstairs.

"What's going on here?" he demanded in a loud voice.

"What's your name?" Ness demanded.

"Dick Howland," the young man replied arrogantly. "My old man's the police captain in this district."

"Well," Ness said bitingly, "that's just dandy. And my name's Eliot Ness and I'm in charge of all the police in this city."

Dick Howland paled and his voice became quiet.

"Look, Mr. Ness, I don't know what this is all about. Sure, I own the building but I don't know nothin' about all this," he pointed to the racing charts and betting slips. "All I know is that I rent this room to a fellow named Nick and I rent the restaurant facilities to a lady named Mrs. Ida Moore."

Ness stared skeptically at Dick Howland.

"It all sounds fishy to me," he asserted. "Where is this guy Nick?"

A short, rotund man stepped forward from among the awed group now standing silently as they listened to Ness and Howland.

"I'm Nick," he told Ness, "Nick McSweeney. It's just as Dick says, Mr. Ness. I rent this room from him all right. He never knew nothin' about what was goin' on here."

Ness looked at him scornfully.

"You mean with all this noise in here that Howland didn't know what was going on?"

"That's right," the fat one muttered, looking down at the floor.

"Get this guy out of here," Ness snorted. "Maybe all he'll get is a hundred bucks fine and costs and I don't suppose that will teach him much of a lesson. But we've got something bigger than that to worry about."

What Ness wanted was to tie up Captain Howland with protection of the building owned by his son, Dick.

"You don't believe all this guff, do you?" Mihailich demanded impatiently.

"Take it easy, Councilman," Ness shot back. "I know what I'm doing. You can bet your bottom dollar that there's more here than meets the eye and I'm going to get to the bottom of it."

Ness had one of his men summon a patrol wagon and the operators, as well as the gamblers, were hustled off to Central Police Station and all of the gambling equipment was seized.

Immediately, on the strength of what had been discovered in Howland's district, he ordered Chief Jacoby to suspend the captain pending a full-scale investigation. This was on a Saturday, and on the following Monday morning Ness declared that he was going to look into all of Howland's financial transactions, including a report that he had put up thirty thousand dollars to help build a new hundred-thousand-dollar night club, the Black Hat.

Ness secretly put his "Unknowns" on the scent and with quiet efficiency they soon gathered evidence from no less than sixty-six witnesses. Their report related a sordid tale of wholesale shakedowns by Cleveland police of the prohibition era. Barney Davis, who was relatively new at this sort of work, couldn't hide his amazement at this police profiteering when he reported to Ness.

"It seems to have been a regular thing for uniformed cops to make the rounds of well-known liquor peddlers and force them to buy costly tickets to clambakes, dances and police benefits under the threat of a crackdown from the boys at headquarters," he declared.

One bootlegger told him: "They went almost too far one day when they asked me to buy tickets for a clambake held the night before."

Even so, he said, he had to pay off—and listen to insults as well.

"What the hell's the difference? You don't go, anyway," the irate cop retorted—pocketing the money the bootlegger finally was forced to give him.

Another bootlegger had told him, Davis asserted with a shake of his head, that police often failed to destroy liquor seized in raids. Instead, they simply sold it back to other bootleggers.

Manski, who had been through the mill in Chicago, philosophically accepted the facts he dug up.

"I paid them at least twenty-five thousand over a five-year period," he was told by one seedy-looking character who claimed to have been a big-time operator in the latter days of prohibition. "Believe me, they took it almost as fast as I could make it."

"They didn't raid us as long as we paid off," another certified. "But the first week we missed a payment or told them we didn't have the money, we got hit."

Still another, who had attempted to operate without protection, said disgustedly: "They framed me with a phony raid when they couldn't catch me. Then they offered to fix the case if I'd kick in."

58

Ness' eyes narrowed as he surveyed the reports and listened to the findings of his undercover agents.

"The average bootlegger didn't seem to make much of a living," he observed caustically. "He apparently had to pay out too much in protection around here to get rich himself."

Just prior to the time Ness was to hand over his information to Matthews for the ruddy-faced prosecutor's presentation to the grand jury, several well-known politicians dropped in to "visit" Ness in his office. They complimented him heartily on "the fine job you are doing."

"It seems a shame about Howland," one of them finally ventured.

An entirely different atmosphere seemed to creep into the room.

"He's a real fine fellow," the politician persisted. "I certainly hope that nothing serious is going to happen to him."

Ness suddenly froze at his desk. He never had enjoyed association with politicians. Now, his blue eyes seemed to bore through the unctuous assemblage in front of him. Ness picked up a pencil and began to doodle on a yellow pad in front of him. He made no reply. This was a trick he had used before whenever he was approached by favor seekers who tried to interfere with the enforcement of justice.

The minutes ticked away leadenly, the silence so heavy that it could almost be felt. There was a general clearing of throats. Ness sat immovable, doodling with deliberate concentration on the pad in front of him. At long last one of the ward heelers stood up and said with assumed heartiness, "Well, I guess we'll have to be going."

Ness never moved. Nor did he answer. He simply kept doodling.

The would-be mediators took the hint. They arose and shuffled silently from the office.

"I should have thrown them out on their ears," Ness said heatedly when he told the incident to Manski.

Now more determined than ever. Ness correlated the information gathered by the "Unknowns" and other investigators, and turned it over to Matthews. The prosecutor, with efficient dispatch, took it before the grand jury and obtained bribery indictments against Captain Howland. Seven others whose names had turned up during the exhaustive inquiry also were indicted. They included Deputy Inspector Oscar P. Black, Lieutenant Charles Orr, Lieutenant Ralph Wingate, Sergeant Joseph Peters and Patrolmen Edmund Teller, William Sterne and Asa Poach.

In succeeding weeks, Howland tried to resign in an effort to save his pension, but Ness fought him and kept him on suspension throughout a four-month investigation designed to lock up the case.

Yet even now all was not completely harmonious in the Ness organization.

Edward P. Ford, Ness' Assistant Public Safety Director, curiously enough made an attempt to have Howland put on pension for life.

After the indictments were returned, Ford made a public announcement in direct and somewhat surprising opposition to the avowed aims of his immediate superior.

"I don't believe they ever will convict Howland. It would save thousands of dollars to accept his resignation," Ford said.

Ness was outraged.

"Every bootlegger in town had to pay off to stay in business," he raged in a manner that was entirely out of character. "More than a million dollars must have gone into the hands of dishonest police. What are we supposed to do, let them go? Nobody is above the law."

The short, stocky Captain Howland was jaunty when he finally was brought to trial. A veteran of twenty-four years in the Cleveland police department. Howland was as flamboyant in his personal life as Captain Drake had been self-effacing. His dark hair had only slight traces of gray at the sides and his bulldog features were set in a perpetual smile. Howland invested in night clubs, restaurants and various other night-life ventures.

It soon became evident, however, that he was fighting a losing battle and the smile rapidly faded. Day by day he huddled deeper in his chair while the case presented by Ness and his "Unknowns" built up against him.

One of the most damaging witnesses was Bartholomew Burke, a middle-aged, graying former truck driver whose left arm had been amputated at the elbow. Burke had been a bartender in preprohibition days and a bootlegger during that period.

Burke had been one of the people uncovered and interviewed personally by Ness and he admitted that only the Safety Director's straightforward and obviously sincere questioning could have pried any information out of him.

Burke explained lucidly the manner in which Ness had prevailed upon him to come forward and testify. The powerfully built man sat stiffly in the witness chair and emphasized his words with sweeps of his one brawny arm.

"Ness treated me decent," he said in a straightforward manner. "He didn't act as if I was dirt, like so many people have done. You got to understand that there are a lot of poor, foreign-born people out my way. Well, he treated them all the same; like they was real people. He didn't use no threats, no rough stuff, and he never acted like he owned the town just because he was the safety director."

Burke cleared his throat noisily and proceeded.

"He'd just come out to my house and sit down like the next fellow. Then he'd say to me, 'Now, Bart, just tell me the truth. That's all I ask. You can't do wrong doing that.'"

In a plain, simple manner which carried an unmistakable ring of sincerity, Burke then told how Howland first had approached him.

"I met Captain Howland in 1928," he said solemnly. "It was in front of my place. He asked me how long I had been running liquor and I told him I'd been at it for about a month. So then he says to me, 'I'm captain of two precincts and I'm going to lay my cards on the table for you to read. It's going to cost you twenty-five bucks a month to run this joint.'"

Howland watched him with slitted eyes, the smile gone from his face, as Burke testified that he had paid him twenty-five dollars the next night while the captain was sitting in his car in front of Burke's place. Thereafter, he said, he paid Howland regularly once a month "for six, seven or eight months, usually while the captain sat in the car."

"Another time he called me up and told me to deliver ten cases of beer to his house," Burke added as if this had been insult to injury, "and he never made no move to pay me for that there beer."

Burke owned a vacant store adjacent to his bootleg joint and he told how he had rented this spot to a man named Fred Grunz. There Grunz brewed illicit beer and he, too, had to pay off to Howland. When Burke told Ness of this, the public safety director had gone to see Grunz to ask him whether he would testify against the captain.

"Not me," Grunz told the young crime fighter. "I ain't gonna talk about it. I don't want to be called no rat."

Ness took the gruff rejection mildly.

"I know how you feel about it," he told Grunz. "But let's go see Burke. I want you to hear what he has to say about it."

They did as Ness suggested and Burke tried to convince Grunz to co-operate.

"Listen," he said, "I told Ness everything already. You can go along with him because he's a good guy. Let me just tell you one thing, I'm done lyin' for the cops."

Grunz stared down at the table top for a few minutes, struggling to make up his mind. Finally, as the other two men watched him silently, he looked up and agreed that he, too, would spill what he knew.

It was plenty.

"I got orders from a cop on the beat that I was to show up at Captain Howland's house," he testified. "I went there and he said that he knew I was making beer. He didn't even ask me to sit down or anything. It was cold turkey."

Howland, he recalled, stood lounging in the front door of his house, one shoulder up against the side of the door, while he asked Grunz: "You're not denying that you're making beer, are you?"

"No, I ain't," Grunz admitted.

"Well," Howland told him smugly, "the privilege of making beer in my precinct is going to cost you thirty dollars a month."

With that, Grunz swore, Howland dismissed him with a wave of his hand.

Grunz related how he then had to go to Howland's home every month to make the payoff.

'I'd say 'How do you do' and then slip him the money."

That went on for several months, he told the court, until his brewery was raided early in 1929.

Just before the raid, Grunz testified, Howland went on night duty. He warned Grunz three days before the raid to "watch your step because I'm going on nights and they might try to slip something over on us."

Four other former bootleggers told similar stories of payoffs to Howland and involved other police officers as well.

At this time in the trial there was a sensational development. Burke accused Howland of engineering a plot to incriminate Ness on charges of having "bought" witnesses.

Burke disclosed that he had been approached through

a couple he had known for years. He visited the couple, and another woman, at a rented apartment on the East Side, which he accidentally discovered was wired with dictaphones. Burke on three occasions visited the two women there and, while serving him liquor, they assertedly told him: "You must have done all right for yourself going along with the police. That Ness must have been pretty good to you."

Burke shrugged expressively.

"They kept egging me on about what I was getting out of it to testify. But the truth is that I once was offered twenty-five hundred to testify for Howland instead of against him. I told 'em that, too."

Howland readily admitted he had the dictaphone records in his possession but denied that he had engineered any such plot. After he had denied everything from the witness stand, his attorney, Thomas X. Francis, contended that a vengeful group of ex-bootleggers had banded together to get their old enemy.

The defense plea fell on deaf ears. A jury of seven women and five men on December 16, 1936 found Howland guilty of accepting prohibition-era bribes.

Howland was ashen as he stood before Judge Luther W. Knight for sentence. Head bowed, he trembled visibly as the jurist imposed on him a two-to-twenty-year term in the Ohio State Penitentiary.

In the rear of the courtroom, his wife Alice collapsed and had to be carried out by attendants. Tears running down her cheeks, one of Howland's daughters spotted Ness as he made his way out of the courtroom. She shouted at him: "Thank you, Mr. Ness. Thank you for nothing."

Ness made no comment, turning silently away from this bitter though understandable tirade.

"There is nothing personal about this case," he explained later. "I'm simply fighting for a principle, that's all."

The law also moved with successful dispatch against those indicted with Howland.

Deputy Inspector Black, a husky, sixty-year-old veteran of thirty years on the force, was identified by seven witnesses as having received regular protection payments during prohibition. A jury of six men and six women on March 10, 1937, found him guilty on five counts of bribery.

Lieutenant Orr, a bald veteran of twenty years of service, had a hung jury in his first trial. But he was convicted in a second trial on charges of accepting prohibition-era bribes.

Lieutenant Ralph Wingate pleaded guilty and was placed on two years' probation.

Sergeant Joseph Peters, the father of six children and for twenty-five years a policeman, was convicted and sentenced to from one to ten years imprisonment.

The three patrolmen who had been indicted were acquitted for lack of evidence.

Assistant Public Safety Director Edward P. Ford, who had criticized Ness for taking Howland to trial on the grounds that he could not convict him, resigned the day after Howland was found guilty.

The Cleveland *Press* greeted Ford's resignation with an editorial which said in part:

In resigning, he shows better judgment than characterized many of his official acts. The year he spent in this position demonstrated conclusively that he was not fitted for it.

The immediate occasion for (his) decision to separate himself from his job appears to have been the publication of a remark he made . . . that there was no chance of convicting Captain Lewis E. Howland and deploring the fact that the public had been subjected to the expense of the trial.

It is pointless to speculate on how much this indicated where (his) sympathies lay or whether he was simply calculating the probable outcome, as anyone might guess on the outcome of a ball game.

(His) demonstration of his unfitness for the post of assistant safety director was already complete through a series of inept blunders.

All of this is said with no ill will toward (him) personally. He had never had any experience actually qualifying him for work in the Safety Department, and he was induced to take the place—perhaps against his own better judgment—on representations that it would be politically advantageous to Mayor Burton to have him there. This turned out not to be so.

It was demonstrated once more that the most advantageous appointments politically are sometimes those in which there is no politics whatever.

To demonstrate that he held no malice, Ness sent Ford a letter of sincere appreciation thanking him for "your contribution to the department's morale and efficiency."

The Cleveland *Press* printed the letter without comment—except that it placed a picture of a bull at the top of the story.

There was, however, a great deal of appreciation for the work that Ness had done to rebuild the morale and efficiency of the department by pressing the Howland case. The Veterans of Foreign Wars presented Ness with a medal as "the outstanding citizen of Cuyahoga County."

The applause brought no let-up in the crackdown. On the heels of the Howland case, Manski's wire tap paid off again when he reported to Ness from recorded telephone conversations that a notorious book in the precinct commanded by Captain Franz Schuyler, had been operating with practically no interference for nearly ten years. It was on the third floor of a corner three-story building and its annual take was estimated to be in the neighborhood of half a million dollars.

"I want you two to turn horse players at the city's expense," Ness told the impassive Manski and the inconspicuous Davis. "I want the whole layout of this place."

Manski and Davis played the ponies for several days and soon had become familiar figures to the employees.

Then Ness called Virginia Allen into his office and told her to fake a telephone call to Schuyler's precinct station. As ordered, she imitated an irate wife.

"My husband lost his pay in that————Street bookie joint. I want something done or I'm going to contact the Public Safety Director and make a complaint to him."

She was assured of "immediate" action.

Each district was under Ness' orders to act with lightning speed whenever it received such a tip.

But as Manski and Davis watched from inside the horse parlor, word was flashed—from the precinct house—that the police were on their way. The bookie operators had the place cleaned up, with all of the equipment removed, before the police from Schuyler's station arrived. Manski and Davis did not tip their hand. But their report showed that the gambling house had been warned immediately while the raid was delayed almost an hour.

Four days later, Captain Schuyler, a fleshy-faced nearly bald veteran of twenty-six years, walked into Police Chief Jacoby's office so unsteadily that the chief promptly suspended him on charges of being drunk.

That cinched it.

Rapidly gathering a squad, Ness dashed to the bookie joint and led a charge up the stairs. Warning lights blinked inside, signaling a raid. But when Ness battered down the door and led his detail inside, Manski and Davis had the operators and some seventy-five patrons lined up quietly under the gentling influence of their revolvers.

Schuyler subsequently denied that he was drunk when he entered the police chief's office and eventually was allowed to resign from the force on a $140-a-month pension.

Despite Ness' continued activities, some who wore and disgraced their Cleveland police uniforms still were not completely convinced. Proof of this came several days later when Barney Davis called Ness on the telephone.

"Maybe this will come as a jolt to you, Chief, but uniformed cops in one of Howland's precincts have been spreading the word that it will be unhealthy for anyone —especially ex-bootleggers—to give any information to you or any of your 'snoopers.'"

That was too much for Ness. On September 1, 1936, he cleaned out the entire personnel of the precinct by transferring every man to other districts and put in his own special crew headed by newly promoted Captain Martin Gillespie. Included in the new personnel of the precinct were a group of young patrolmen carefully selected from the ranks by Ness and organized into a special detachment known as the "Minute Men."

Organization and action—plus the aid of the "Unknowns"—were beginning to pay off.

CHAPTER 5

AS TIME WENT ON, NESS CONTINUED TO PROVE TO BOTH the good and bad elements of Cleveland that he deserved his "Untouchable" reputation. Slowly, but unwaveringly, he began to move against the mob.

Two of the leading gathering places for the mob were a pair of notorious gambling casinos in the suburbs of Cleveland. One was the raffish "Boston Club"; the other the "Bailey Club."

The authorities long had been trying to close them down, but with no success.

This job had been attempted several times by John Matthews, a man dedicated to enforcing the law. But it was a sheer stroke of fate and happenstance timing that Matthews, a large man in his mid-fifties, decided to make one more determined effort to shutter both casinos one month after Ness took office in Cleveland.

These gambling spots were outside the jurisdiction of the Cleveland police department and Matthews knew that he could obtain no official assistance from that source. He did, however, arrange for the raiding assistance of twenty men from a private detective agency. These operatives, when they met with him, were sworn in as deputies and divided into two squads.

"We're going to strike both places simultaneously," the ruddy-faced Matthews told Assistant County Prosecutor Clifton Miller. "We'll hit them both at once and hit 'em hard. I want all the equipment seized and I want the operators. We're going to close them down for good this time."

Matthews had hired two moving vans to transport the deputies to their respective stations. He and Miller took half of the men and proceeded to the "Bailey Club." The remaining deputies, under the prosecutor's chief assistant, Paul E. MacAdoo, set out for the "Boston Club."

With both raids timed to be sprung simultaneously at 5 P.M., the two legal spearheads separated and converged on their respective targets at the agreed hour.

Matthews, Miller and their group of deputies pulled up in front of the "Bailey Club" right on the dot of five o'clock and poured from their van. Matthews led the way to the front door and hammered vigorously for admittance. The door was opened a few inches and an arrogant lookout examined the county prosecutor and then surveyed the men grouped behind him.

"Waddaya want?" he spat out.

"I'm the county prosecutor," Matthews snapped.

"Well," he was told, "you can't come in without a membership card."

"This is a raid," Matthews told him.

With this he waved a sheaf of warrants in the lookout's face.

The official papers made no impression on the guardian of the gambling house portals.

"That don't mean nothin' to me," he retorted. "I'll have to see somebody about this. You'll just have to wait right here until I get back."

Before Matthews and his aides could make a move, the lookout slammed the door in their faces.

And such was the state of law in Cleveland and its environs that Matthews and his deputies stood there quietly and waited for the man to return.

The deputies shuffled their feet back and forth and muttered to each other in low tones. Matthews' face began to turn brick red as they waited five minutes; and five minutes more.

"Are we the law, or ain't we?" asked one of the deputies in the rear.

It was too much for a burly, six-foot deputy with a long-since broken nose who looked as if he might have been a former prize fighter.

"The hell with this," he said. "Who the hell do they think they are, ignoring warrants and keeping us waiting out here?"

With that, the giant with the battered face picked up a wooden bench standing near the door and hoisting it over his head began battering it against the closed door. Splintered wood flew from the groaning panels of the door and the noise of the pounding reverberated inside like the beating of a drum.

"Okay, okay," a voice yelled from the inside.

While the deputy stood there motionless, the wooden bench which had served as a battering ram poised over his head, the door was flung open and the grumpy lookout stood in the doorway again.

"Listen, you guys, I been tryin' to get somebody to talk to you," he blustered. "You'll just have to wait a little while longer."

"The hell we will," grated the big deputy, dropping the bench to the floor of the porch with a crash and grabbing the lookout by his coat front. "You're coming out and we're going in."

He hauled the startled man onto the porch and hurled him into the arms of two other deputies with instructions to "take care of this monkey." Then the raiders poured inside in Matthews' wake.

"A real swinging operation," Miller shot at Matthews as they crowded through a small reception room and entered the main gambling salon, where almost five hundred customers were shooting craps and playing blackjack and roulette at a number of tables. It was a cosmopolitan crowd with a large percentage of women and a number of these, judging from their dress, obviously were from the upper strata of local society.

Matthews stopped just inside the main salon, with Miller and the deputies behind him, to survey the scene. So feverish was the "action" around the tables where the gamblers were banked three and four deep that for a few moments the intrusion went unnoticed. Then, as the deputies continued to jostle into the room, even the most frenzied gamblers were attracted by the noise and confusion.

"Everybody hold it," Matthews shouted in a voice which carried above the uproar. "This is a raid."

A woman screamed and the throng began to push toward the door but Matthews' deputies blocked the exit and the employees were taken into custody.

"The rest of you can go," Matthews told the patrons, and they scuttled from the premises as the deputies began to confiscate the gambling equipment.

"None of the big wheels are here," Miller reported to Matthews with disappointment. "These mugs are just working stiffs."

"Too bad," Matthews observed. "But one thing sure, we've closed up this joint at last."

At the "Boston Club" it was another story.

When MacAdoo's group of deputies mounted the front steps and pounded at the door for admittance they met immediate resistance. In answer to MacAdoo's pounding a beady-eyed lookout wearing a tuxedo opened the door a crack and peered around the edge with a deep scowl on his face.

"Waddaya want?" he growled imperiously.

"Open up," MacAdoo shouted. "This is a raid."

MacAdoo threw his shoulder against the door but there was a chain across the inside and it refused to yield.

"Oh, no, you don't," snarled the man with the malevolent eyes, producing a pistol which MacAdoo could see through the crack. "Anybody who tries to get in here gets his damned head shot off."

Ignoring the pistol, MacAdoo peered through the narrow opening in the chained door and caught a glimpse of a large room. The interior, he saw, was jammed with several hundred people. But before he and the deputies massed around him could throw their weight against the door and snap the chain the door was slammed abruptly in their faces.

Frustrated, MacAdoo stood on the porch silently contemplating what he should do while the deputies waited behind him.

"I guess," he shrugged, "we'll have to break down the door."

"What'll we use to bust it in?" one deputy demanded.

The decision was taken out of MacAdoo's hands right then as a black touring car drew up to the curb and three men leaped out and raced toward the porch.

The leader was John (Jackie) Powers, described in one of the warrants as an operator of the "Boston Club." The two burly men with him, bulges under their tuxedo jackets indicating that they were wearing guns in shoulder holsters, were his bodyguards.

"Jackie," a stocky, moon-faced man, panted up on the porch. He was red-faced and anger showed in his tightened lips.

"What the hell are you guys doing here?" he demanded autocratically.

MacAdoo faced him and said, "This is a raid ordered by the county prosecutor."

Powers shouldered his way roughly through the deputized group surrounding the doorway, his two gunmen at either shoulder, and stuck his chin in MacAdoo's face. He looked at the deputies with disdain.

"You guys," he grated, "had better get the hell out of here before you find yourselves in real trouble. You mess around here and somebody's liable to get killed."

MacAdoo and his deputies gaped at "Jackie's" effrontery. And while they stood there, Powers squeezed between the bulk of his two cold-faced bodyguards and gave a sharp signal rap on the door. The chain inside jangled immediately, the door flipped open and Powers and his two hoods slipped quickly inside. MacAdoo and his deputies could hear the chain being replaced after the door was slammed in their faces.

"What do we do now?" one of the deputies asked querulously.

MacAdoo led them off the porch and onto the front lawn, where they gathered for a council of war.

"Well . . ." the prosecutor's chief assistant began, but got no farther. For at that moment the front door to the "Boston Club" was thrown wide-open and the round-faced Powers strutted out onto the porch. Arrogantly he faced the officers, feet spread and fists knotted on his hips.

"Let me tell you guys something," he shouted. "If any one of you bastards tries to stick his neck in that door we'll shoot him down. We've got machine guns and damned if we won't use 'em."

It appeared that this was no idle threat, because just behind Powers stood the two thugs who had accompanied him into the club and each of them held a submachine gun at the ready.

Powers stood staring at them defiantly and then shouted: "Now get the hell out of here before you get hurt."

The bemused forces of the law retreated to the sidewalk followed by Powers' raucous laughter and, as they trooped dispiritedly away, Powers and his men went back inside and slammed the door behind them.

MacAdoo rallied his men on the sidewalk and they were

standing there, debating what should be done, when Matthews and several of his aides arrived. Greatly agitated, MacAdoo filled him in on the details of the frustrated raid and dumped the situation back into the prosecutor's lap.

"There no use standing here like a bunch of whipped schoolboys," Matthews observed. "Let's go down there," he pointed to a gasoline station on a nearby corner, "and decide what we should do."

They trooped bitterly to the gasoline station and Matthews held a council of war with Miller and MacAdoo. They debated various courses of action while the deputies milled around outside.

"If we make a move against the place," Miller cautioned, "those hoodlums are certain to start shooting and some of our men might get killed. After all, these are only agency men and I don't know how much we can count on them."

Matthews nervously wiped his rimless glasses. "The only thing I know to do," said the prosecutor, "is to see if we can get some help from the sheriff."

While the assembled deputies waited, Matthews went inside the gasoline station and attempted to contact Sheriff Leon Voltzmar by telephone. However, the sheriff was ill in bed at his home. Chief Jailor Jackson F. Short volunteered to contact the sheriff and shortly thereafter called Matthews back. The jailor was apologetic.

"The sheriff says you should call the mayor of the village if you think you need help. He says to tell you that this is in accord with his home-rule policy."

The white-haired sheriff had inaugurated a no-interference "home-rule policy"—with each village privileged to run its own police affairs unless it specifically requested his help—when he had taken office five years earlier. Thus, in all that time, Voltzman never had attempted to close down the "Boston Club" and neither had the local authorities.

Matthews next desperately attempted to reach the village mayor but that official was not at home.

"What do we do now?" Miller puzzled.

Suddenly, Matthews' face brightened.

"I don't know if he can help us or not," he said, "but let's call Eliot Ness."

An urgent call was made to Cleveland city hall and Matthews was advised that Ness was attending a meeting of the city council.

"Please tell him that its vitally important that I talk to him immediately," Matthews said.

Matthews waited impatiently and, after some delay, he heard Ness on the other end of the line.

The words, coated with exasperation and indignation, poured out of the county prosecutor as he gave Ness a detailed account of the raid.

"Is there any way you can help us?" Matthews asked desperately.

"I'm not certain," Ness said. "You know, of course, that you're completely out of my jurisdiction."

Matthews' voice was subdued.

"I know that," he sighed. "But how in the name of decency can any law-abiding citizen stand by and see the law pushed around this way?"

"Well," Ness replied, "let me see what I can do. I'll call you right back."

While Matthews and his aides sat impatiently in the gasoline station, Ness hurried back into the Cleveland council meeting. Going right to Mayor Burton's chair, he leaned over the mayor's shoulder and in whispers told him of the situation at the "Boston Club."

The mayor listened with a perplexed frown. It seemed obvious that he didn't understand how this affected him, the city of Cleveland or Eliot Ness.

"I just don't see what we can do about it," he shrugged.

But the mayor, looking up as he made this observation, was surprised at the change in Eliot Ness. The pleasant, smiling face was cold and hard. The calm, blue-gray eyes were icy. The lips were flat and straight.

"Listen," Ness told him huskily, "I took this job to bring some law and order to this area. I just can't stand around while hoodlums make a mockery of the law. How can we ignore the fact that these lice were carrying machine guns right in broad daylight?"

The mayor nodded agreement.

"You're absolutely right," he said. "Maybe we can't step in officially but you can go as a private citizen."

Ness didn't even bother to reply. He was already wheeling and racing from the council chambers.

Leaping into his car, he sped to Central Police Station and there he stalked into the squad room just at the time when the policemen were changing shifts. The casual conversation and banter of the squad room ceased as Ness entered.

"I need some volunteers," Ness said tersely and without explanation as his eyes swept the room. "I only want those who are going off duty."

There were no questions. Three plain-clothes men, five motorcycle officers and twenty-eight patrolmen immediately stepped forward and volunteered their services.

Ness' voice was low and steady.

"There's just one thing," he said as he laid it on the line. "No uniforms and no guns. We're going to show a bunch of hoods that we don't need arms to handle their type of rat. And," he paused to let it sink it, "we're also going out of our jurisdiction to do it."

The volunteers looked at each other in silent speculation. But not a man backed down.

The department long had been ashamed of its reputation for being "on the take." The tarnish of a straying few rubbed off and sullied the names of all of them. Now they had a glimmering hope that at last things might be different. So they were quick to demonstrate that they were solidly behind Ness, ready to back him to the limit.

"We'll need about five squad cars," Ness barked to one

of the officers. "Order them up right away and if anybody asks any questions I'll take the responsibility."

Those few still in uniform quickly completed their change into civilian garb while Ness impatiently but silently paced the squad room floor. When they were ready they filed out and climbed into the squad cars. Then, with sirens screaming and Ness leading the cavalcade they sped to the gasoline station, where Matthews greeted them with great relief.

"I certainly am glad you could make it," he said.

Ness was all business.

"Give me the details," he said.

Matthews told him how MacAdoo had been repulsed orginally and how "Jackie" Powers' thugs had threatened the deputies with their machine guns.

"There's no question in my mind but that they'd shoot, too," Matthews admitted. "They've had things their own way around here for a long time and they don't care about anything or anybody. They think they can beat any kind of a rap, even murder, and," he added ruefully, "I've got to admit that they've even done that. So there's no reason to think that they won't open up with all the artillery they've got if we do charge the place."

Ness nodded and frowned as he looked through the wide windows of the gasoline station and saw several hundred curious onlookers lining the sidewalks.

"Get these people back out of here in case there's any shooting," Ness directed curtly. "We don't want anybody hurt."

The crowd was moved back and Ness, deploying his own men from the Cleveland police department around the outside of the gambling house, turned to Matthews and snapped: "Let's go."

Eliot Ness did not wait for company. Even before the rest of them could get into motion, he had charged ahead and mounted the front porch steps of the "Boston Club."

"Keep your eyes on those windows," he directed some of his men scattered across the front of the house.

Then, an easy target in his tan trench coat, Ness raised one foot and gave the door a violent kick. The force of the blow tore off the lock, springing the door, but it still was held by the safety chain inside. One more expert kick snapped the chain and the door flew open. As it did, a man stepped in the breach and leveled a pistol at the taut-faced Safety Director.

He reckoned without Ness' hair-trigger reflexes and training.

Ness was a jujitsu expert. Faithfully he had studied and practiced its bone-breaking intricacies for three nights a week ever since his graduation from the University of Chicago.

Now, as often before in his explosive past, he proved as quick as one of the six cats he had at home. Ness, who admitted quietly that he "could throw a man thirty different ways," leaped forward. Knocking aside the man's pistol hand, with one swift movement he disarmed the hoodlum. Then, before his opponent could move again, he hurled him to the floor.

"Okay," Ness called back through the door to the approaching Matthews, "go serve your warrants."

But by now it was far too late. Once inside, the raiders found little more than a huge bare room. During the more than five hours of siege, and while the private detectives had fretted at the corner gasoline station, the patrons of the club whom MacAdoo had seen through the door had completely vanished. Gone, too, was "Jackie" Powers and his two machine-gun-toting bodyguards. And, what Matthews could not understand, all of the smaller gambling equipment and practically all of the larger pieces of apparatus also had disappeared.

"We had the place watched the whole time by a couple of the men and they didn't see a soul come out, not even the customers," Matthews told Ness. "I simply can't figure out what could have happened to the gang and to their equipment."

"There must be some answer to it," Ness said and set off to prowl through the house.

Carefully he combed the interior, looking cautiously into one room after another. Then, as he passed one of the rear rooms on the lower floor which had a sign, "Men," he heard a faint noise inside. Ness silently pushed open the door and saw a man standing in front of a mirror casually combing sleek black hair. It was a rather large room, Ness saw, the tiny washbasin and a single toilet in on corner looked strangely incongruous.

"What are you doing in here?" Ness barked.

The man shot him a contemptuous look and finished combing his hair before he replied: "It don't take no genius to see I'm combin' my hair."

"Well," Ness snapped, "comb it outside where we can ask you some questions."

The man turned insolently and headed for the door, ramming Ness with his shoulder as he went past. It was a mistake.

By this time, Eliot Ness had absorbed all of the gangland insolence he could stand. Spinning the man around by the shoulder, he unleashed a punch to the chin that drove the hoodlum back against the wall. Then, when the thug made no move but simply stood there glowering, Ness searched him swiftly only to find him unarmed. Struggling to control himself, Ness grabbed the man's lapels and threw him violently aside.

The swagger was gone from the mobster now as he realized that this was a different breed of cop than those he had known. This man, he could see, was fighting a battle with himself to keep from working him over. As Ness hurled him aside, he stumbled and fell heavily against the toilet.

Ness stared in amazement as the toilet skidded out of the way under the weight of the gangster's falling body and revealed a swinging panel in the wall. This man obviously had been left behind to put the toilet back in place and make certain that the panel was concealed.

Just at this moment, Matthews and one of the deputies walked into the room and Ness told them: "Put this monkey under arrest."

Then he plunged into the gloom of the narrow opening and found a secret corridor stretching in front of him. Feeling his way slowly, Ness followed its twisting path until he emerged through another door and found himself outside in a rear alley which led onto the next street. It was quite obvious that the gang, well prepared for just such an emergency as Matthews' raid, had sent the customers out this way and also had used the passageway to cart off their gambling apparatus.

Stumbling back through the dark corridor, Ness emerged once again into the men's room where Matthews was waiting.

"That's the rathole," he told the surprised prosecutor.

"That's the way they got out and how they made the apparatus disappear. You should have had the whole place surrounded."

"Well," Matthews protested, "the houses on the next street back right up to these and I never thought there'd be a way out from the rear."

Ness nodded.

"You couldn't be expected to know about it."

"Tell me one thing," Matthews asked, pointing to the narrow opening of the secret passageway, "how in the world did you ever find this?"

"Just lucky, I guess," Ness grinned, rubbing his knuckles.

As they left, both of them agreed that as a crimebusting operation, the raid on the "Boston Club" had been a fairly complete dud.

And yet it had served several purposes.

For one thing, it created a powerful alliance that night between the young Cleveland Public Safety Director and the forceful Cuyahoga County Prosecutor which was to make them the greatest crime-fighting team in the city's history.

It also developed in Ness' men a new-found respect and admiration for his courage.

Even more important, it served notice on Cleveland's underworld that Eliot Ness was a pretty special breed of Boy Scout.

CHAPTER 6

THE "BOSTON CLUB" RAID WAS MERELY THE KICKOFF IN A
long and bitter struggle with the all-powerful Mayfield
Road Mob. But even in what was an abortive police move,
Ness had proved to the gangland powers that he was out
for blood.

On the day after the "Boston Club" raid, Ness declared
open warfare on the mob. There was a new look to him
now.

Sitting before the roll-top desk in his headquarters next
door to the mayor's office, Ness crisply ordered the lid
clamped down on the numbers game "as it never has been
before in this city's history."

"Each precinct captain will be held absolutely responsible for his district." The soft voice left no question about
Ness's rock-hard intent. "That way, there can be no passing
of responsibility from one officer to another.

"I want to shut them down not so much on moral
grounds but because gambling and big money breed crime.
I want every man in this department to know that I have
yet to find a situation for which there is no legal remedy.

I intend to harass these lawbreakers until they will be glad to get out of this city."

There was another purpose to his plan. Ness was laying the groundwork for a drive to clean out crooked cops who were "on the take."

Still, it was clear even to Ness that more than words would be required to accomplish his objectives.

Ness proved that he meant what he said in his gambling edict: that same night he led a raiding party which took 150 men into custody at a policy drawing.

There followed, for a few days, a strange period of calm in the city of Cleveland. But then the Cleveland *Press* reported that the word had been passed to resume operations and it published the addresses of twenty-three gambling spots which had gone back into business.

The gamblers were betting privately that Eliot Ness would be busted out of office the first of March.

Among the places named by the *Press* was a gambling establishment which masqueraded as a cigar store and barbershop. The *Press* charged that this place was operated by Marvin Schwartz, a brother of one of the city councilmen.

The public-spirited newspaper gave the list of the gambling spots to Ness personally, even though he was ill at his home with grippe at the time, handing it over to him before the first editions hit the streets. Ness immediately advised his office by telephone to have raiding units crack down on *all* the places listed.

These raids were a fiasco. Of the twenty-three spots raided only one was found to be doing business. There was no evidence of any gambling in the other places, including the one allegedly operated by Schwartz.

Ness received heated denials to all suggestions that someone in the police department had tipped off the places which were to be raided.

"The time that elapsed between Ness's orders to raid the places and the time the raids were conducted was too short," Ford said, "to cover them up if there actually was gambling going on in those places."

Back on his feet again, Ness personally led a series of quick raids and this time they were productive. They were crowned by a full-scale assault on the headquarters of Horace Mann, the man known as Cleveland's "Policy King" before the Mayfield Road Mob moved in and took over supreme command. Mann and his brothers, Junius and Delbert, were taken into custody along with three others. Ness and his raiders also seized an adding machine, two hundred clearing house slips, incriminating rolls of adding machine tape and other data.

All six of the prisoners, however, were released by Police Prosecutor Bernard W. Day. He insisted that he could not hold them because no search warrant had been obtained before the raid.

"Had the police proceeded in the proper manner it would have been possible to make a case against Mann and the others," he ruled. "However, I have found that entrance to the place was made without a search warrant."

Ness appeared unconcerned over the decision. The raid had been designed as a probe to find out how policy was operated rather than an all-out attempt to nail Mann. It was merely part of his planned over-all investigation before inaugurating a sweeping campaign.

At about this time, Cleveland radio station WJAY imported a radio broadcaster from New York City. With three local men writing the show, it began a program called "The Ghost Reporter."

The "Ghost" campaigned vigorously against the gambling setup and one night even gave a list of fifteen bookie joints that the police were planning to hit in "surprise" raids the next day. Obviously there was no surprise—and only one of the fifteen was running when the raids were made.

A week later, the home of the man who owned and managed the station was bombed. No one was injured but the explosive, placed in a basement window well, did about five hundred dollars' worth of damage.

"We'd hate to have to mess you up, too," an anonymous letter warned Ness. "Let this be a lesson to you."

The radio station manager blamed the bombing of his home on the gamblers—retribution for the activities of the "Ghost Reporter," who had given names and addresses in rather spectacular style during the three weeks the program was on the air. The station promptly dismissed the program's three writers.

"I've got a family to protect," the manager said. "I don't want them hurt."

The next night the "Ghost Reporter" made his last broadcast.

The "Ghost" said in his farewell sign-off: "I expected retaliation personally but we are fading into the atmosphere not because we fear these sinister influences but because innocent lives have been jeopardized."

Ness traced the bombing back to the mob but was never able to apprehend the man responsible. He apparently had left town.

Meanwhile progress was being made in other places. Ness expressed pleasure with what he called his "precinct control."

"It has accomplished much in the gambling situation even though I do not think it is one hundred per cent efficient," he admitted. "Complaints have continued to come in. My objective is to put an end in this city to mob control by those who attempt to collect revenue from those who violate the law."

With this statement, Ness startled the bookies all over town—who had been expecting the usual "mild lid"—by again ordering his police captains to "really clean up this town and keep it clean."

He dictated a full-scale crackdown on everything: bookies, policy, prostitutes, "suspicious persons," the works.

"For the first time in six months I now am able to devote my entire time to this project," Ness said. "I am holding the officers in charge fully responsible and this responsibility is going to be a real one."

Lieutenant Sidney Greenspan, later to be promoted to captain and then to deputy inspector, soon proved to be the department's biggest nemesis of bookies. He was a forceful, independent thinker who, in subsequent times, frequently stumbled into hot water with Ness because he had a more zealous devotion to his individual duty than he did to diplomacy when it came to dealing with his superiors.

Ness could grin and bear it, for he admired Greenspan's effectiveness as a crime-fighter more than he deplored his lack of tact, and he permitted Greenspan to operate on his own initiative. This was one of the traits which always endeared Ness to his men.

Two others who quickly drew Ness' attention were Detective Sergeant Mark Jackson and Patrolman Jerry Vickers. They were youthful, collegiate types, both blue-eyed, and they looked like freshly graduated college football stars. They, too, were the kind of enthusiastic and energetic police officers Ness prefered.

Within one month after their assignment to Ness' office, they stormed more than forty gambling establishments and arrested twenty-one alleged operators. The top arrest they made was that of Heimie Norton, heralded as one of the city's largest policy operators.

"It's very dangerous work," Jackson jokingly told Ness.

"Dangerous?"

"Yes, but not because of any shooting if one of us is spotted in these joints," Jackson quipped. "In the excitement after they notice us somebody's liable to be trampled to death in the rush to get outside."

"Great," Ness grinned, "let's make them want to get out and stay out. If we really keep the heat on, maybe those people with the gambling itch will keep away and we can put a real crimp on the operators' incomes. Once we drain off their incomes, the battle's half won."

And "keep the heat on" they did. The gambling flying squads were accountable only to Ness and they revelled in their freedom of movement. As a sample, on just one day:

Jackson's squad raided ten bookie joints, battering down doors and storming inside to put ninety-six operators—and customers—under arrest.

The French Club on a main thoroughfare had been raided often. But Captain Andrew Brigsmith surrounded it with his squad, broke in and made a shambles of the place. The doors were boarded up when the raiders finished and twenty people were hauled into court.

Vickers got word of a bookie parlor on the third floor of a building in downtown Cleveland. Carefully he blocked all the exits, including the stairs and the fire escape. Then, operating in plain clothes, he stood by until a customer approached the door, knocked in a peculiar manner, and was admitted without question.

"Let's try the same knock," he chuckled to one of his men.

They did, and also were admitted without question.

"Okay," Vickers snapped, pulling his pistol, "this is a raid. Line up against the wall."

Fifty men and two women were herded downstairs into patrol wagons and carted off to the police station to be booked. . .

Yet it was the lack of judicial action against habitual violators whenever they were arrested which annoyed Ness in these early days.

Nothing seemed to happen in the magistrates courts.

The worst offenders were given ridiculous hundred-dollar fines. Not a single bookie or other person charged with gambling was even committed to the workhouse. More than half of the total fines levied were suspended. Seven convicted gamblers with long records were given workhouse sentences but these were suspended on their ludicrous promises to give up their occupations. Fifteen others had their cases continued, and nothing more was heard about them.

Ness was extremely irritated over hauling in lawbreakers and then having them escape with what amounted to a mild reprimand. So he next instituted a plan by which all patrons picked up in a raided establishment not only were required to go to police headquarters to sign statements concerning what they had seen but they also had to supply a personal "biography" which, it was announced publicly, went into the department's "gambling file."

This discouraged the criminals from frequenting bookie joints for fear of being picked up and held on old charges.

It also was a deterrent to many of the so-called "decent" citizens who felt that it was nobody's business but their own if they elected to play the ponies or bet policy. The new Ness edict meant that the police had a file on them at headquarters. And this was a bit of notoriety from which most honest people flinched.

Thus once again was Ness able to hit at the purse strings of the gambling operators.

One of Cleveland's most notorious gambling figures at this time was Benny Silver, a short, swarthy, dapper man reputed to stand high in the inner circles of the Mayfield Road Mob. Silver had been a key figure in the Cleveland underworld since the prohibition era and boasted of being a man of great influence.

His earlier career bounced back against him in May of 1937, however, when he and a cohort named Pete Greenstein, along with ten other defendants, were placed on trial in federal court on charges of defrauding the government of taxes on the sale of illicit whiskey.

This ordinarily would not have concerned Ness in his new position, although he had been one of the federal agents to compile the evidence against the gang, but he was annoyed with Silver's and Greenstein's arrogance in running a gambling joint behind a fake cigar store front in Cleveland.

"It's bad enough that they're doing it while they're on trial," Ness told Mayor Burton, "but can you imagine that these monkeys have the nerve to visit this joint during the noontime court recess?"

"Are you sure of this?" Burton asked.

"Don't worry about my facts," Ness told him. "I've got it straight."

Ness knew this because he had one of his own men inside as a "customer." This operative was Peter Clayton, a promising young probationary policeman.

At each noon recess, Silver and Greenstein grabbed a bite at the Hotel Olmsted lunch counter and then before returning to court moved on to their gambling joint. One day, Ness took two plain-clothes men and fell in closely behind the pair without attracting their attention.

Then, when Silver and Greenstein entered the gambling place, Ness and his men walked right in behind them, nodding in friendly fashion to the lookout as if they were with Silver.

Greenstein, a square-jawed cigar-smoker whose favorite pose was to stand with his thumbs hooked into the armholes of his vest, spotted Ness at this point. But the door into the back room already was open and Ness and his men bulled their way past a second spotter and into the main gambling room.

"Nice to see you, boss," young Pete Clayton said to Ness as they placed all the occupants of the room under arrest.

"How the hell did you get in here?" Silver demanded. "Who okayed you in the first place?"

"You did," Clayton grinned delightedly.

One of the customers, overhearing the byplay, pointed a finger at Greenstein and sneered: "How come you always tell me I'm as safe here as if I'm in church?"

"Who me?" Greenstein replied. "Say, I just came in here to get a cigar."

Clayton, who had been cleaning out the gamblers' supposedly secret arsenal, interrupted this protest.

"That's a joke." Then he turned to Ness and told him, "That cigar counter is a fraud. They've only got a few real cigars. The rest are dummy boxes to make it look good."

Ordered into waiting police vans along with two employees and eight customers, Silver and Greenstein didn't go quietly.

"You can't hold us," Silver insisted. "We're due back in court right now."

"Tell it to the judge," Ness said. "The judge I'm taking you to see."

They were released on bail later in the afternoon and, when they returned to court, Silver and Greenstein through their attorney asked for a mistrial on the grounds that the jury had been prejudiced by the noontime raid.

"Sit down and be quiet," Judge Hiram B. North told them in dismissing their claim. "You'll both be better off if you do."

Silver, along with eleven of his henchmen, was convicted in federal court on the fraud charges on May 16.

But shortly thereafter, as Ness returned to his home late one night, the mob struck back. He had left his automobile in the driveway and was walking toward the front porch when an automobile appeared and cruised down the street toward him. It slowed as it neared the Ness house. Light from a nearby street lamp glittered on a gun barrel and, as the gun chattered, Ness threw himself in a rolling, headlong dive behind a clump of shrubbery which was the only place of concealment, poor as it might be.

Rolling still deeper into the bushes, Ness drew his own .38 caliber pistol from its shoulder holster and lunged to his feet. As he did so, he came up firing, squeezing off three snap shots at the would-be assassins' automobile. He was rewarded with the sound of shattering glass.

That was enough for the mobsters. The car leaped forward and disappeared into the night.

Ness stood there silently for a few moments, the night crowding in around him, and then slid the pistol back into the shoulder holster. Emerging slowly from the trampled shrubbery, he was brushing dirt and leaves from his clothes when the porch light went on at the house next door and a neighbor appeared.

"What in the world was all that noise?" he demanded in great agitation as he saw Ness.

"It appears," Ness replied mildly, "that car certainly was backfiring. Quite a bang, wasn't it?"

With that, he quietly said good night and walked on into his house, leaving the neighbor staring after him.

Eliot Ness had been a target often enough before so that the incident didn't shake him up too much. He was even a bit elated over it. At least now he knew he had the mob worried.

CHAPTER 7

WHILE THE POLITICIANS STEWED, NESS CHOSE, AFTER
careful deliberation, the man to succeed Ford as his assistant. He picked Elwood Pierson, a young lawyer and former
state representative.

Pierson, a tall, rangy, dark-haired man whose long jaw
was overshadowed by a small mustache, at one time had
been a neighbor of Ness.

"I'd kid him about his work as a federal agent," Pierson said, "so one time he invited me to go along on an
alcohol raid. I'll never forget how he pushed open the door
and busted into the place. He didn't know what was behind
that door, and he didn't seem to care. He just doesn't know
what fear is."

During this time, of course, Ness never lost his determination to run the Mayfield Road Mob permanently out
of business. It was a period punctuated by a rapid-fire
series of gambling raids which kept the underworld, the
newspapers, the police department and the entire city in
constant turmoil.

These were not advertised raids in which the police

approached with screaming sirens. Usually the gambling joint had been well cased by one of Ness' undercover men or by one of his "Unknowns." Then, at the busiest hour of the book's operation the door would fly inward under some heavy police brogan or a scientifically applied shoulder, and those who sought a back way out would find themselves covered by a smiling "horse player" who actually was an undercover man. Ness smiled with satisfaction over the fact that the mob was getting panicky when his telephone rang one night and a harsh voice muttered: "Ness?"

"Yes," he replied.

"This is a guy who would like to be a friend. No, don't talk. Just listen. How would you like a grand a week to knock off these raids? They're getting to be a nuisance."

Ness grinned to himself. "Only a thousand dollars a week?"

"What the hell do you want," the voice growled, "the mint?"

Ness' reply was quick, clipped and hard: "No, I don't want anything from you monkeys. You don't have enough money to buy me off."

"Okay," the voice threatened. "Remember you asked for it. And you'll get it."

The line clicked dead and Ness hung up the receiver with slow speculation.

He knew he would have to watch his step. The rats were getting desperate.

An attempt to make good on the threat wasn't long in coming. The very next night as Ness left his office, he felt that something was wrong. He was even more than usually alert as he started to cross the street in the middle of the block. Suddenly, out of the corner of his eye, he saw a parked limousine leap into motion and hurtle toward him. Either they were trying to run him down or, as the car moved past, there would be a sudden burst of gunfire.

Ness spun on his heel and made a leaping, rolling dive which carried him under another parked automobile as the black limousine swept past. As it did so, he rolled back out, tugging at his pistol as he leaped to his feet, but the car tore through a red light at the next corner and turning, disappeared from sight.

Ness looked ruefully down at his oil-stained suit and at the torn flap hanging from one knee. But, he reasoned as he cautiously crossed the street and entered his own automobile, a damaged suit and a skinned knee were a cheap price to pay for his life, And, starting tomorrow he vowed to himself, the gambling raids would be stepped up to make them pay in spades for this latest attempt on his life.

Meanwhile, as he drove home, his mind returned to one of the other jobs ahead of him, and one of those closest to his heart. This was the problem of juvenile delinquency, which had increased at a frightening rate in Cleveland.

Ness had laid out a plan to tackle the youth problem and, as was to be proved subsequently, had done so with astonishing foresight.

Even at the height of his investigations, when he needed every policeman on whom he could get his hands, he had asked for seven volunteers from his department to take training as Scout masters.

New troops of Boy Scouts, he theorized, would get the kids off the streets. Eventually he set his newly formed Scout groups up in precinct houses which were abandoned when he motorized the police department almost completely.

"What we've got to do," he insisted, "is to make friends of these friendless kids and show them that the world isn't against them."

There was, of course, opposition to such "coddling" but Ness, bucked at several turns, insisted: "For years we have been spending millions of dollars to cope with adult crime by arrest, prosecution and confinement. Yet we have done little to deal with the juvenile problems which are the source of adult crime."

As a starter he had his police make friends with young toughs in an effort to show them that the impudently scorned "cop" could be a friend.

"Our attempt to work through the Boy Scout movement failed in some areas," he finally was forced to admit. "Something else was needed in areas where groups of the same nationality tended to gather together, and Cleveland is a city with many such groups.

"The eventual answer was our Boys Town program. The project reduced juvenile delinquency sixty-two per cent—and even greater progress can be expected in the future."

Ness formed a special juvenile bureau under Captain Adam Gold to study youth crime and crime potential in the city's worst areas. Then, with all of the statistics at hand, Ness and Gold issued an invitation to forty-five gang leaders to attend a peace-making dinner. They had hired a hall in a tough gang-ridden area, where almost every house contained one or more youngsters listed on the books as a "J.D."

Fifteen minutes after the dinner was scheduled to begin not a single boy had appeared.

Puzzled by the apparent boycott, Ness and Gold stepped outside to see what was going on. They saw at once that the boys, standing in scattered and wary groups on nearby corners, were watching the building and each other with great suspicion. An ugly mood was building up.

"They think they smell a trap," Ness told Gold. "There's only one thing to do. You go one way and I'll go the other and we'll talk to them and see if we can't convince them to come in."

One by one, Ness and Gold buttonholed the hostile, watching groups of boys and assured them that there would be no police roundup. First one gang, then another, slowly began to drift toward the hall and within a short time they had all filed watchfully inside.

It was a tense situation. Gang leaders traditionally are

almost always at swords' points among themselves. It is the way of the underworld that gangland rulers are the dog-eat-dog enemies of rival chieftains, and these boys were carbon copies of their elders. Even after their cautious entry into the building, they sat and glared at each other until the food was served. It was a solid and appetizing meal—one such as many of them had never enjoyed —and it could not be ignored even if it meant the sacrifice of their hostility.

After the meal was over Ness started the brief after-dinner speeches.

As a means of introducing himself, he told them stories of action during the Capone era in Chicago, a sure-fire attention-getter under any circumstances but a guaranteed fourteen-karat attraction here. He recalled the scene with the satisfaction of a job well done.

"After that I analysed some of the recent juvenile delinquency jobs. I gave them the actual figures: how much money these juvenile delinquents had made when you counted reform school and jail terms. I didn't preach right or wrong. I just talked dollars and cents, explained the problem as it affected all of us—them and the city—and asked them what we all should do about it. I had a roll call and they each got up to give their ideas.

"What came out was what we already knew. The great majority wanted to earn their money but they couldn't hold down jobs because of their discredited reputations or the stigma of their relatives or their infamous neighborhoods. Further, they had no recreation centers to provide an acceptable outlet for their energies."

An organization was formed on the spot. The forty-five leaders were to be the "Big Shots."

"This is going to be no goody-goody club," Ness told them. "I detest sissies—and you'd better believe it."

They laughed. He was their kind of guy.

It was, in the beginning, a sort of supergang.

But the unofficial head of the gang was Eliot Ness. That made the difference.

After lining up jobs for some of the oldest of the leaders, Ness called another meeting.

"I'm going to ask you for only one thing," he told them. "I want you boys to clamp the lid on this illegal stuff for thirty days to prove to me that you mean business."

It was considered a minor miracle when there wasn't a case of juvenile crime in the area for a whole month.

This example of what could be accomplished with faith and effort was magical. Public support provided funds to equip club rooms, and in no time at all, job offers began to roll in.

That was how the Cleveland Boys Town plan was born. Soon each of ten different Boys Towns had its own mayor, police chief, court and other officials. Recreation areas were provided and the boys deserted the streets for hobby classes and sports. And most important for the older boys were the booming job placement bureaus.

As the movement gathered momentum, the various groups generally were installed in abandoned precinct houses, where they used most of the facilities—except for the cell blocks. The older boys promptly removed these, gleefully wielding acetylene torches on the bars behind which some of them had once been confined.

Working with the boys, directing the undercover operations of his "Unknowns" and keeping the anti-gambling pressure on constantly, Ness seemed inexhaustible as he found time to move into ever new channels of operation.

One of his greatest ambitions was to cut the appallingly high total of traffic deaths.

"We spend a great deal of time and money trying to solve crime and murders and attempting to get murderers convicted," he declared. "But the Number One killer in Cleveland is the automobile. Somehow we must reduce the slaughter in our streets."

Shortly before Ness became the city's Director of Public Safety, Cleveland was ranked second by the National

Safety Council—not as the second safest big city in the United States but as the second most dangerous. Only Los Angeles had a worse record of traffic fatalities.

In 1936, a year in which Ness was all but overwhelmed by his investigations of police bribery and probing inquiries into labor racketeering, Cleveland motorists were mowing down their fellow citizens at a fantastic rate—23.5 deaths annually per 100,000 population. And the city then had a population of 900,000.

New York and Milwaukee, the safety leaders, had an average of only 11.7 deaths per 100,000 per year.

Through Ness' efforts, within only two years, Cleveland was named co-winner with Milwaukee as the "safest big city in the U.S.A." And in 1939, Cleveland won the honors all alone, the undisputed "safest city in the U.S.A."

The task of educating the citizens to the need for caution on the streets and highways, as well as the problems of enforcing laws, weren't solved overnight.

Yet when the results began to show, they were little short of spectacular.

In 1937, when Ness instituted the beginning of traffic control by modern methods, 240 men, women and children were cut down by cars within the city limits.

In 1938, the toll was slashed to 130—a saving of 110 lives.

In 1939, the toll was cut farther to 115.

The major blow struck for traffic safety was the almost complete motorization of the police department. In December, 1938, Ness achieved his greatest mass reorganization —installation of two-way radios in prowl cars and division of the city into zones which placed a policeman within fifty-five seconds of any spot in town. In addition to the two-way radios in prowl cars, he inaugurated a police teletype system between Cleveland and other major cities. The result:

"In a year," Ness reported in December of 1939, "felonies were reduced twenty per cent and major crime, including robbery, showed a drop of nearly fifty per cent. The over-all crime rate was down thirty-eight per cent."

A single telephone number—Main 1234—brought immediate assistance for any citizen needing emergency help. This was the telephone number of central radio headquarters.

In the pre-Ness days, a citizen in distress called his local precinct, if he was lucky enough to know what precinct he happened to be in, and received help if there happened to be someone lounging around precinct headquarters who could take the call. Otherwise, people called "downtown" and waited until the cop on the beat looked in while making his rounds.

The new setup was brought home with great impact to the public in the summer of 1939.

At 4:40 A.M. the police radio droned these words:

"Calling car 525—car 525—go to the Glanz Fur Company at 10615 East Euclid—1-OH-6-1-5 Euclid—Burglar alarm."

One minute later car 525 pulled to a screeching halt in front of the Glanz Fur Company building. The prowl car cops leaped out just in time to collar a thief coming out through a smashed window with an armload of furs.

A second car took the thief away. Car 525 went back on patrol.

Elapsed time: three minutes and fifty seconds.

In November of 1939, another incident:

An emergency call was received reporting prowlers at the Auto Car Sales and Service Company at 1961 East Sixty-first Street. Four minutes later it was all over. An ex-convict resisting arrest had been shot and killed by police, and his accomplice was under arrest and on his way to jail.

Cleveland had installed the first licensed police radio station in the nation more than ten years earlier. But like most major cities, it had used only one-way radio—from the station to a few cars—to handle major emergencies.

The two-way system inaugurated by Ness was completely revolutionary because it opened up new possibilities of teamwork. Central radio acted as a clearing house and individual cars could indicate immediately if they needed assistance.

As another forward move, Ness increased the motor-cycle force. Then he gave all his traffic officers a set of forms which violators had to sign, guaranteeing bond for appearance in court to answer a summons. He also had the police spread the word to minor offenders by way of warnings—not tickets—that "we are trying to save lives, not put people in jail."

In one of his first moves after taking office, Ness denounced the practice of sending supposedly poor police-men to "Siberia"—as the traffic division was known.

"We want our best policemen on traffic duty, not our poorest ones," he proclaimed.

The "Untouchable" soon fired up all his traffic men with his own zeal. Speedily they realized that they did not have to, nor could they, "fix" traffic tickets for offend-ing politicians, friends or even relatives.

Revenue from traffic tickets soared immediately. In the first six months of the Ness regime, a total of $38,130 was paid in traffic fines. A similar six-month period before he took office netted less than half of that amount.

Ness also ordered that all "scofflaws"—drivers with many tickets which they had ignored—be brought in by the police.

He commanded that drunken drivers be examined on the spot and either be formally charged with drunken driving or be released as innocent. The practice of tossing them into the cooler until they sobered up was abandoned. They were either guilty, and stayed, or were innocent and were set free.

Seemingly in a thousand places at once, Ness arranged with a group of judges to set up a single traffic court. In this court the judges conducted hearings only on traffic cases, taking turns in rotation, one month per judge per year.

"This is essential," Ness maintained. "It gives our judges an opportunity to concentrate on serious problems and not just to sit in on an occasional traffic case in between some other headlined cases."

Ness spearheaded an arduous campaign against jaywalking.

He fought hard for auto inspection because "We find that too many accidents are caused by broken-down jalopies which shouldn't even be on the road, or by cars with faulty brakes."

He conducted a "saturation" publicity campaign by newspapers, radio and personal public-speaking appearances each and every time the city introduced a new traffic law.

He ordered all prowl cars painted in bright colors so that they would serve as a warning on the streets.

In 1940, he had his police knock on every door in the city to hand out printed pleas to "help keep Cleveland the safest big city in the U.S.A."

In the fall of 1940, with the co-operation of scores of Cleveland businessmen and merchants who footed the bill, he placed a full-page advertisement in the Cleveland newspapers which featured shocking photographs of fatal traffic accidents and their bloody victims. The heading read:

"32,000 died this way last year—115 in Cleveland.

"This is what the ambulance driver saw. Don't YOU be the next to paint the scene for him."

Cops at busy intersections passed out cards to jaywalkers which read:

Warning

You have just crossed against a red light. This is a very dangerous practice that has resulted in 33 deaths and 324 injuries in 1937. Stop saving seconds and losing lives.

Obey traffic and safety rules.

It is better to be safe than sorry.

Co-operating merchants paid for huge cloth banners which Ness had installed over many railroad viaducts and overhead passes saying:

Your next accident may be your last.

Other banners placed elsewhere read:

Cleveland values your life—protect it.
Walk sensibly—drive carefully.
Cleveland Police Department Safety Campaign.

The man who made his reputation as a crime crusader confessed privately that he thought the automobile was more dangerous than any mobsters he had ever met.

"The problem created by the automobile will always be with us," he reflected. "Only the constant vigilance of the public will help us keep down the toll of accidents in our city's streets. None of us can be satisfied with the progress we have made because even one life lost in traffic is one too many."

Slowly but surely, Eliot Ness was making progress in all directions. But his traffic accomplishments were his proudest.

"This work," he observed, "probably is the most important I have ever done."

CHAPTER 8

TO FURTHER COMPLICATE NESS' PROBLEMS, A LABOR RACK-eteering war began to erupt in 1936. It began with the fatal shooting of Eddie Blackman, bargaining agent of the Feed Wagon Drivers' Union.

Blackman, a blustering, brawling roughneck known as Cleveland's toughest labor union leader, was hated and feared by many people. This six-foot-four-inch bruiser weighed a muscular 250 pounds and was accustomed to settling any and all arguments with his fists.

The forty-year-old tough had just kissed the youngest of his three daughters good night in their bedroom. He then went downstairs and sat down in an overstuffed easy chair just beside the front window in his brightly lighted living room. Three minutes after that final kiss, a gun roared outside the closed window, only inches from where he was sitting, and Blackman's head was almost torn from his body by the force of the blast from a twelve-gauge shotgun charge.

There were, aside from his family, few mourners. But his violent end was a bloody sign of things to come.

The connection between Blackman's death and the investigation which Ness at about this time had started into labor racketeering never was fully established. But, shortly thereafter, Ness disclosed that his investigation had uncovered forty-five cases of extortion at the Northern Ohio Food Terminal in Cleveland.

Producers hauling in food to the terminal were shaken down; farmers and truck drivers were blackmailed almost openly, and, when they resisted, were badly beaten. When the haulers did resist, bombs were planted in trucks or hidden in cargoes; vehicles were wrecked and tires were slashed to ribbons.

"This is nothing but a gang of outright racketeers operating under the guise of labor unions," Ness proclaimed.

Farmers bringing in their own crops to sell at the terminal were told that they could not unload their own trucks. A "Marketers Co-op Club" met them at the terminal and advised them they would have to hire two-man crews for the unloading process at forty-five cents per minute of working time. "Dues" were collected both from those who delivered the produce and also from the merchants who were buying it in this two-headed racket.

Ness, angry over what he called "undisguised blackmail," formed a "Vandals Squad" under tough, two-fisted Captain James J. Bradley.

"I want your men to infiltrate the food terminal disguised as loaders and stall workers," Ness ordered. "Arrange it, too, so that some of them drive in trucks loaded with produce. The first thing we have to do is to stop this terrorism. Then we'll get our hands on the racketeers who are behind it."

The Vandals Squad went to work with a vengeance. The first break came when two undercover men, dressed as a truck driver and his helper, wheeled a load of produce into the market and were accosted by a band of thugs demanding that they be hired for unloading purposes.

"I think we can handle it ourselves," said driver Frank Smith, a patrolman who had been a Golden Gloves boxer.

"Well, in that case, we'll unload your whole rig right here," said one of the toughs. "And you two guys, too."

The hoodlum took a roundhouse swing at Smith and was knocked flat. The rest of the toughs leaped toward Smith and his fellow officer but from all quarters the ready members of the Vandals Squad appeared and the racketeers were a well-battered crew when they found themselves in a patrol wagon.

It only required a few such incidents with the Vandals Squad to clean the hoodlums completely out of the terminal area. And, with this crew on hand for constant protection, more than a hundred witnesses stepped forward to substantiate seventy overt acts of vandalism and bribery which Ness, moving with ruthless precision, handed up to Prosecutor Matthews for prosecution.

For by this time, Matthews had been elected city prosecutor and was working closely with the energetic young crimebuster. Although Ness was a Republican who rarely mixed in political maneuverings, he actually had helped to swing his election. He had stumped for his Democratic friend even though Matthews was in opposition to Mayor Burton, the man who had hired the boss of the old Untouchables.

With typical forthrightness, Ness had gone to Burton before the election.

"Hal," he told the mayor, "I have to help all I can to elect Matthews. I know that the Republicans to whom you naturally are committed have a good man. But this goes beyond mere party lines. I feel Matthews is the best man for the job and, as long as I have to work so closely with the prosecutor, it is my duty to help get the man I want in the job."

Burton surprisingly gave Ness his wholehearted approval.

"Naturally, I hope we get our man elected," he said.

"But, Eliot, I know how much doing a good job means to you and I want you to feel free to do whatever you think is necessary."

Ness had campaigned vigorously and successfully. And now, with Matthews installed as an aggressive city prosecutor, Ness knew he would get the immediate action he wanted when he did hand up criminal information.

But cleaning up the blackmail and extortion at the food terminal didn't satisfy Ness. He set his Unknowns into action to see whether other labor racketeers were operating in Cleveland.

They laid bare a sordid situation.

Ness' secret squad of three—Manski, Davis and Virginia Allen—went into action with its usual stealth. They talked to builders and contractors as a starter and came up with a long history of "shakedowns" in the building trades.

Barney Davis was frankly amazed at what he called the "perfidy of people."

"We've found out that building contractors have been forced to pay from fifty dollars to three hundred dollars per job in construction blackmail," Davis said with a shake of his head. "These payments were made because of threats by a guy named Mickey Worthington, bargaining agent for the Builders' Union, either to pull a strike or to prevent strikers he already had called out from returning to work."

"Not only that," added Manski, "but he also threatened to make 'trouble' by causing damage to buildings under construction."

"Were they damaged?" Ness asked.

"They certainly were, Eliot," Virginia Allen confirmed. "It's strange, but men like to tell their troubles to a sympathetic woman. Well, that's me. I'm the world's most sympathetic woman. I've got a whole list of jobs on which there was trouble, complete with names and dates and prior threatening conversations with Worthington.

When they didn't pay up their machinery was ruined, interiors were vandalized and ripped up and supplies were destroyed."

Manski interrupted to add: "This thing seems to have been going on for at least five years. It's a wonder somebody didn't report it a long while ago."

Ness's Unknowns then turned over to him a list of twenty-five witnesses, nineteen of them contractors, all of whom after full assurance of protection had told either Davis, Manski or Virginia Allen that they would testify. Always one to double-check his information, no matter how reliable the source, Ness called in several of the volunteer witnesses to clear up some minor points.

"Did Worthington give you any reason for demanding this money?" he asked one contractor.

"Yes," said the man, "he told me and several other contractors of my acquaintance who had similar trouble with him, that the sums he asked were simply a 'contribution' toward a carpenters' unemployment fund."

Ness called Manski and told him to check on the supposed fund.

"There's no record of any such fund," Manski reported back.

Another contractor told Ness that, when he was unable to pay, Worthington took his payment "in trade."

"I wasn't able to meet his demands for money," the man told the Public Safety Director. "So I was forced to make up for it by having one of my crews work for three days finishing two rooms in the attic of Worthington's house—for free."

One of the most co-operative witnesses was Elbert C. Princeton, a contractor from Lakewood, Ohio. He had had an argument with Worthington and the labor leader, in a fit of anger, punched Princeton on the nose. The Unknowns had visited Princeton shortly after this incident and found the contractor in a retributive mood.

"Sure, he blackmailed me," Princeton roared. "I've had to pay him a fifty-dollar tribute on each and every house I've built. Now on top of everything else he comes around and strong-arms me. Damn right I'll testify. Not only that, I'll give you the names of some other guys he's been bleeding."

Princeton was as good as his word and, with a heavy file of information against the building trades leader, Ness went to Matthews and they obtained indictments against Worthington on five counts of blackmail.

As far as the Cleveland public was concerned, the Worthington case was small-time until June 8, 1937, when Worthington failed to appear for trial and was declared a fugitive. In fleeing from Cleveland he also had forfeited the two thousand dollar bail in which he had been released.

Further investigation showed he had fled to California, where it was discovered that he had joined a builders' union in San Francisco under an assumed name. Apprehended there by the Federal Bureau of Investigation he threatened to "expose the whole racket in Cleveland."

Worthington was subsequently returned to Cleveland on September 1. Then, on October 25, after nearly two months in jail because he could not raise the increased bail on which he was held, Worthington in a surprise move pleaded guilty to five counts of blackmail. He was sentenced almost immediately to a term of from three to fifteen years.

This was not the end of it. Because, as Ness pursued his investigation of Worthington's racketeering activities, the evidence against others began to snowball. The "Unknowns," headed by Jim Manski and Barney Davis and other former Untouchables now working elsewhere but still ready to lend their former chief a hand, began conducting mysterious interviews in several cities including New York, Pittsburgh, Chicago and Kansas City.

Ness was rarely at his desk in city hall from the end of October until mid-November. Throughout most of 1937 he devoted almost all of his efforts to investigating the labor rackets and vandalism, except for a hectic two-day siege, July 26-27, during which violence flared in a strike by C.I.O. unionists against the Corrigan-McKinney division of the Republic Steel Corporation.

On the night of July 26, Ness was forced to dispatch squads armed with tear gas and riot sticks to quell a six-hour running battle between strikers and nonstrikers at the steel plant. The violence flared intermittently along Broadway, Independence Road and other streets surrounding the giant mills. At the height of the riot, five hundred nonstrikers streamed out of the Independence Avenue gate and rushed toward a group of one hundred pickets. They met head on and a wild melee broke out.

When it was over, 125 had been injured in the worst outbreak of the two-month-old strike. To prevent further violence, Ness ordered establishment of a "peace area" around the plant. Pickets were forbidden to come any closer than five hundred yards to any portion of the mill. A gaping, jostling crowd of three thousand, many of them onlookers, gathered at the plant the next evening but the tension gradually subsided.

With this taken care of, Ness again concentrated his full attention on the labor racketeering investigation.

Only Ness and a handful of his top agents had the faintest idea of what was developing. To those on the outside, Ness seemed to be conducting routine business for the city. He made frequent trips out of town, once to Boston for what he described as a speaking engagement, and again to Milwaukee, presumably to get advice from traffic officials in what then was the "safest big city in the U.S.A." He took long weekends, too, and even the constantly watchful city hall reporters, who conceded that Ness was one of the most tireless workers they had ever known, agreed that Ness finally had been forced to slow down.

Actually he was conducting a thorough and complete inquiry into the careers and machinations of two long-time labor racketeers—Bob R. Donalds and James A.

McCray—which was to develop into one of his greatest gangbusting coups.

Donalds, a stocky man, at this time was vice president of the Carpenters' District Council and bargaining agent of the Glass Workers' Union. Normally a good-humored man, he had a reputation for being extremely tough when aroused.

He had been arrested in 1914 on a pickpocket charge and had beaten a burglary rap in 1915. Sent to the penitentiary as a parole violater, he was later released. Four months after his release he was found innocent of carrying concealed weapons. His next arrest came while he was prominent in labor circles and working as an organizer for the Glass Workers' Union. He was charged with malicious destruction of property. He was acquitted. There were five later arrests, all without convictions.

No glass was set anywhere in the city without Donald's permission. If a builder did go ahead without authorization, union workers were summarily called off the job. If a builder had the temerity to employ non-union workers, a barrage of stench bombs or—in the case of plate glass —a well-aimed brickbat followed. Donalds at last organized his own glazing company and then the builders not only had to pay tribute for getting a job done but had to buy their glass from Donald's company.

McCray was a wiry man of forty-three who stood half a head taller than Donalds, but his rather slender figure had, as a monument to good living, a magnificently proportioned paunch. He, too, had been arrested frequently but there were no convictions against him.

McCray first had been charged with an antitrust violation in 1930 in connection with an alleged racket which reportedly forced barbers into a "protective" association and which also made an attempt to elevate and fix prices. He had been arrested on the same charge in Dayton, Ohio, two weeks after that. Both times the charges were dismissed but the arrests had to drive McCray out of the "barber" business almost immediately.

Later on, he had organized a window washing union in Cleveland and at the time of the Ness investigation was president of the Builders' District Council representing two thousand workers. At one time this had been one of the largest building trade locals in the city and in 1937 it was still a powerful factor both politically and financially.

Donalds was more notorious for the stench bomb and the brickbat technique, but McCray often used similar tactics.

The names of both labor leaders had been mentioned frequently in connection with a tidal wave of window-breaking during the years from 1934 into 1936, when nearly ten thousand windows were smashed. The frustrated police never had been able to tie the pair in with either the window-smashing or any type of labor racket.

Charles Bellevue, who had been the Safety Director in 1934, once became so incensed over the depredations that he ordered a twenty-four-hour watch on the two ring-leaders by two-man teams of detectives working three, around-the-clock shifts. This led to what became known in Cleveland as the "Big Parade," a brazen and raucous ridicule of the forces of law and order.

It hadn't taken Donalds and McCray long to realize that they were being "tailed." Nevertheless, they felt so secure that they were amused rather than worried.

"Just for kicks," they made it a practice to take long drives into the countryside in a powerful automobile, stepping on the gas so that the detectives following them in an older-model car would have to pursue them at a fender-shaking, teeth-rattling pace. Occasionally, they would get so far out in front that they would lose the trailing plain-clothes men. With the "fun" of the chase gone, they would wait by the roadside or dawdle along until the detectives finally came into view. Then, off they would go again.

When they were in the city, the pair would ride around casually and then unexpectedly wheel into an alley and disappear. The trailing policemen, lacking the horsepower to match the pace of the two sneering racketeers, fumed at their impotence.

Throughout this riotous preamble, McCray and Donalds gleefully were hatching up the scheme for the "Big Parade" with which they intended to "show up" the police department. They finally pulled it off on a sunny spring day in 1934—at the stroke of noon—when they knew that their gallery of appreciative spectators would be at its greatest.

McCray and Donalds obtained two Packard touring cars with uniformed chauffeurs and had the collapsible tops battened down so that there could be no concealment of the passengers. In the first car they placed a small but extremely noisy band of musicians. On the front bumper of the lead car, reaching from fender to fender and extending above the radiator, they posted a huge square placard which proclaimed:

Engaged in a silly
Three-ring circus
Donalds and McCray
As the stars
Who are they shielding?

On both sides of the first car were other gaudy signs which announced:

McCray and
Donalds'
Circus
Animated by the Cleveland
Newspapers and Police Department

Riding importantly in the second car, resplendent in formal morning attire—glistening top hats, striped trousers, cutaway coats, pearl gray spats, vests with white piping and Ascot ties neatly furled under wing collars—came Donalds and McCray.

There was—as they knew there would be—a third car

113

in the cavalcade. This one was the small, battered sedan carrying the two sheepish, embarrassed detectives who had drawn the tailing duty that day.

As the parade moved slowly up busy Euclid Avenue, with noonday crowds lining the curb, the band struck up the mocking strains of "Me and My Shadow."

Donalds and McCray, sometimes with feigned solemnity and again with impish high glee, tipped their hats to the onlookers.

When the motorized procession reached East Fourth Street, another crowd was gathered around two taxicabs which had been in a collision. McCray, spotting the shattered windows in the cabs, wisecracked loudly and brashly to policemen investigating the accident: "There ain't supposed to be no window smashing today, boys."

Al Capone, told of the "Big Parade" while he was languishing in Alcatraz where Eliot Ness had helped put him, said: "Why didn't I think of something like that?"

The police, however, had the last laugh that day—partial revenge for all of the "tailing" indignities which they had suffered.

Safety Director Bellevue, when he learned of the "Big Parade," turned purple with rage and shouted to his aides: "I want those bums thrown in jail. We'll give 'em something to laugh about. Give them the full treatment. Don't grab them until city hall is closed for the day. That way we'll be able to keep them in there for a while before there's any pressure."

Having issued these orders about Donalds and McCray, Bellevue ordered flying squads of policemen to the lake-front area to pick up the "dirtiest bums you can find." Anyone who looked as if he had had a bath in the previous three months was allowed to go free. Fifty of the saddest vagrants the police could find were herded into paddy wagons and taken to the Central Station.

Donalds and McCray, picked up on spurious charges, were hustled from one outlying precinct to another. Finally, after city hall had closed, they were taken to the

Central Station and tossed into the bull pen along with the malodorous fifty. Then, on that hot May afternoon, the steam was turned on, full blast, in every radiator in the cell block.

McCray was correct. There were no windows smashed that day—even though the two labor leaders, and even the unwashed half-hundred, must have felt like breaking every window in the jail.

By the time they were "sprung," Donalds and McCray were limp and bedraggled, their parade finery sadly wilted.

Yet, despite this incident, they soon were back doing business at the same old stand.

CHAPTER 9

ON JUNE 19, 1936, IN HIS FIRST SEMIANNUAL REPORT, NESS was able to advise city officials that vandalism had taken a headlong tumble.

"There were eighty-nine cases of vandalism in the first six months of the year compared to three hundred and nine for a similar period in 1935," Ness said statistically.

But then, as his investigation of the Northern Ohio Food Terminal terrorism disclosed, the labor racketeers mistakenly believed that Ness was too preoccupied with police corruption, the Mayfield Road Mob gambling clean-up and his countless other duties, including the drive to make Cleveland a safer city. So once again they began to turn the heat on.

Thus as Ness pursued his inquiry into Worthington's racketeering, the evidence against Donalds, McCray and others started to mount. The whole investigation, as it developed, required nearly a year. But once he had turned loose the "Unknowns" and his other investigators on the careers of long-untouched but suspect labor leaders, the facts began to emerge.

Ness and his secret group operated strictly on the theory that "there is safety in numbers" and they convincingly sold that idea to prospective trial or grand jury witnesses.

"I won't call any of you to testify at any time unless there are twenty or thirty others who have agreed to do the same," was his stock promise, and one which he kept to the letter. "And we will give you all of the protection that you need at any and all times."

The determined and exhaustive interrogation had turned up considerable information against both Donalds and McCray, and yet there was nothing solid enough for a conviction until Ness learned the background of a series of labor disputes which had struck the Mitchell restaurant chain in the middle of 1936.

Following a routine check of the disturbances, Ness made it his business to develop a social acquaintance with Ronald and Neil Mitchell, who had developed a large restaurant chain from a small lunchroom. There were several Mitchell restaurants in Cleveland as well as others throughout the country.

As they got to know Ness, and his steel fiber, the Mitchells eventually confided to their attentive friend that Donalds and McCray had accepted payments of fifteen hundred dollars to smooth over labor problems involved in opening the newest dining room in their chain.

Ronald Mitchell told Ness that they had contracted to spend one hundred fifty thousand dollars on the remodeling with contractors who were using nothing but union labor. They also had been leasing the premises since January 1 at a monthly rental of fifteen hundred dollars and with that amount of money involved were very anxious to get their new establishment opened on schedule.

"But only four days before the work was to have been completed," Ronald Mitchell told Ness, "the painters and glaziers were called off the job. The place was absolutely windowless."

This was the situation when, on May 1, 1936, Donalds

and McCray showed up at the restaurant. Ronald talked to Donalds alone.

"I told him I had talked to the other officers of our company and that, since we were to open in five days and wanted the glass put in, we had decided we could pay as high as six hundred dollars to have the glass placed."

"That's not enough," Donalds replied. "I got to have two thousand."

"Well, we have to go ahead, and although I'm not authorized to agree on this we might pay fifteen hundred. If you agree to take it I'll go back and tell my people," Mitchell countered.

Donalds finally had agreed to take the fifteen hundred.

Mitchell discussed the payment with his father, and the agreement was made.

At this juncture Donalds called in McCray and they discussed how the payoff should be made. Donalds suggested that Mitchell should "take a ride with McCray and give him the money."

"I've already been taken for a ride," Mitchell told them heatedly.

The restaurant owner said he later went down to union headquarters and handed the money directly to McCray.

"Do you want to count it?" Mitchell asked sarcastically.

McCray shook his head.

"No, I'm not interested."

Mitchell then narrated to Ness that he had told McCray he needed someone to wash the restaurant windows. He suggested that McCray, as a person interested in a window union, might have some idea of what company he should hire.

"Here's one that's just starting in business and I'd like to see them favored," McCray said, pulling from a drawer in his desk a list of companies approved by his union.

The payoff worked, Mitchell related, and the glaziers, as well as the painters, went back to work the next day. The restaurant opened on schedule, and stayed open until about nine o'clock that night. However, sometime during the early hours of the following morning, two bricks were hurled through the large front plate-glass window.

Ronald Mitchell wrathfully headed for Donalds' office and confronted him with the window-smashing episode.

"Well, now, Mitchell, about this business of busting glass and so forth, I think we can get rid of that for you but it will take some money."

"How much?" Mitchell asked.

"Oh, about the same as before," Donalds replied.

The indignant Mitchell refused to make any more payments.

Possibly as a result of his adamant stand, on June 30 a second Mitchell restaurant was hit by a devastating stench bomb and on July 23 another brick sailed through the window of the chain's new eating house.

This descriptive account, along with all the other evidence which had been gathered against the Donalds-McCray faction, was enough for Ness. On November 25, 1937, he turned over his information to the grand jury charging blackmail, extortion and general conspiracy by the two prominent labor leaders. Under Prosecutor Matthews' fiery direction, the grand jury on December 18 returned a three-pronged indictment. It charged:

1. That Donalds and McCray prevented installation of plate-glass windows in the remodeling of a Mitchell restaurant unless the Mitchells paid them money and that Donalds and McCray threatened also to pull painters off the job unless the money demanded was paid.

2. That Donalds and Fritz Nemecek, alias Mike Reilley, extorted $475 from Bernard Heinz on the threat of pulling glaziers off a job for the Abrams Stores, Inc.

3. That Donalds and John F. McVeigh extorted $35

from Gabriel Henlein to speed installation of a window at the Stratford Shop.

Nemecek was the business agent for the Painters' Union and McVeigh was an assistant business agent of the Glass Workers' Union.

Some of the out-of-town witnesses were reluctant to return to Cleveland, figuring that Ness was doing a routine cleanup job and nobody in the world would be able to convict the labor racketeers there because the situation had been so impossible for such a long time. Others thought that because certain of the payoffs were for minor individual sums the prosecutor never would be able to get a conviction.

Ness, in his irresistible way, convinced them that they were doing a necessary and worth-while public service.

He also quartered them secretly in their hotel rooms under heavy police guard.

Both Donalds and McCray loudly protested their innocence, and at the trial Donalds asserted that as a union leader it was his duty to go to the aid of other unions.

"The Garbage Collectors' Union had been making no headway with Mitchell and that's why my glaziers were called off the job, not to force a payoff but to assist other unions in their negotiations," Donalds testified.

"Mitchell finally agreed to negotiate, saying, 'We have to have the place opened and, if that's the only way, I will sign an agreement with the garbage collectors.' We took his word for it and the glass was put in," Donalds contended.

Later, the broad-shouldered Donalds said, Mitchell refused to negotiate with the garbage collectors.

"I told Mitchell he was pretty cheap to get the glass put in and then refuse to negotiate," Donalds protested. "I told other union members I guessed we were licked because Mitchell never intended to negotiate."

About halfway through the trial, defense attorney Hugh S. Berryman went to the bench and requested Judge Judah F. Pennock to bar Ness from the courtroom because he was "impressing" the jurors merely by his presence. The jurors were sent from the courtroom while counsel for the defense was making the objection. The judge swiftly denied the motion, ruling that "The jurors should be no more impressed by Mr. Ness than they are by anyone else in this courtroom."

Although the Mitchell affair was the one on which Donalds and McCray were being tried, Prosecutor Matthews introduced other evidence and more witnesses to "similar offenses" to clinch his case.

Indicating the complete thoroughness of the Ness investigation was the wide range of substantiating witnesses which the prosecution summoned.

One of these was Nels W. Gustafson, head of a New York construction company which in 1935 did some work at two locations in Cleveland.

Gustafson testified that, although he employed members of the Glass Workers' Union, he was approached by Donalds and was ordered: "Sign up with the Glass Cleaners' Union or you won't get your glass installed. You have a good job here—but no window-washing contract, no glass."

Gustafson declared that he sought out McCray and agreed on a window-washing contract. While he was talking with McGray, who happened to be on a picket line in front of an apartment house at the time, Donalds showed up.

"Now that you gentlemen have settled all the big things, lets get down to brass tacks," Donalds asserted. "I want some money."

"You got what you wanted," Gustafson answered. "We have agreed on a window-washing contract."

Donalds snorted.

"Didn't you ever pay off under a railroad bridge? I want five hundred."

Gustafson said that at this point he began to bargain, first offering fifty dollars. Then, when he offered one hundred dollars cash, Donalds accepted it on the spot.

But later when he asked Donalds to approve some overtime work, Donalds roared: "This is a hell of a time to ask for concessions. This will mean overtime—and fifty dollars more."

Gustafson said that he paid it and—adding insult to injury—Donalds then asked him for a nickel to make a telephone call.

Ness brought Albert Fernow all the way from Syracuse, New York. Fernow, foreman for a Syracuse contractor, said that he had paid a hundred dollars to a Donalds representative to get glass installed in a job he had done in 1936.

Paul B. Mansfield, Cleveland manager of the Youngstown Plate Glass Company, certified that he frequently "held up" installation of glass until he received approval from Donalds' office because he had learned from experience that "when we sent glaziers out to do a job they were stopped and it cost us money." He added that he kept a "blacklist" book in his office containing jobs which were being "held up" on orders from Donalds.

"I had a hold-up order on the Mitchell restaurant because Donalds told me it was an unfair job," he testified.

Witness after witness bravely answered Ness' summons.

Gustav Swenson, installation superintendent of an Evenston, Illinois, furniture works, said under oath that he paid a man designated by Donalds a total of two hundred dollars so that work could be resumed on installation of glass mirrors on a job he had handled for a downtown department store late in 1936.

Milton T. Burley, proprietor of André's Fashion Shop on Euclid Avenue said his firm gave a hundred dollars to get glass installed because Donalds told him some previous painting and glass work in the store had been non-union work.

Edward H. Sayers, operator of an ice cream store, revealed that he had surrendered fifty dollars in cash to

Donalds. Sayers affirmed that in 1932 he and an unemployed cousin painted a storeroom. While they were working, three men came in and told them that they had better employ union men. Sayers replied that he could not afford it.

"A few days after these men came to visit me, two large panes of glass were broken in my store front," Sayers asserted. "I called the insurance company but did not get the windows in. I had to board up the front for two months. Finally I had to go to Donalds' office and pay him a fifty-dollar 'assessment.' "

Dimitri Nokuchni, a butcher on West Sixteenth Street, told the jury that windows in his shop had been smashed and he was unable to get them reinstalled because of Donalds' orders. The union leader shrugged that he was powerless to rescind his orders because some of the store's fixtures had been put in by nonunion labor.

"You are fined sixty dollars," Donalds told him. Then, it was testified, Donalds settled for three ten-dollar bills which he stuffed in his pocket without giving Nokuchni any kind of receipt.

Nonunion fixtures again were given as the reason by Donalds and McGray for halting work at a Euclid Avenue clothing store in 1932, said Nathan L. Walters, a fixture company executive.

"They asked me to pay them five hundred dollars for the benefit of unemployed union members or the work would have to be done over," Walters said.

Eventually, the issue was settled for $150 cash to each of them—although there was no unemployment benefit fund in the union.

When it was all over, eighty-five witnesses had given their testimony. Of this number, forty-five appeared for the prosecution and thirty-seven for the defense.

Ness had won another feather in his cap when the jury convicted both Donalds and McCray on March 8, 1938. They were sentenced to terms of from one to five years and, to their own as well as the city's vast astonishment, were ord..red to prison immediately.

Judge Pennock left no question as to how he regarded the defendants.

"I want to forestall any attempt to free these men by Court of Appeals proceedings. They'll not go free on bonds. In all my twenty-five years on the bench I have not seen anything like this trial. The defendants even attempted to influence the jury. They got husbands and other relatives of the jurors to come into the courtroom and talk with them (the defendants). These men are dangerous to the community and there is reason to fear organized reprisal if they are left at large."

With indignation, the judge at this time revealed that on the second day of the trial, Ness had detected a swiftly aborted plot to "fix" one of the jurors.

Ness had learned that an undisclosed ally of the men on trial had flown to Chicago to raise a "defense fund" to finance their trial. It was learned that the sum of fifty thousand dollars had been sent back to Cleveland on the day the trial opened. Ness' investigators were told that the money was to be used to reach a woman who was expected to be a juror. The defendants planned to get to her through her husband, who was in a business which brought him into contact with Donalds.

When they heard of the plan from Ness, the prosecution had the prospective juror dismissed without disclosing that he knew of the proposed "fix."

The trial of the two labor leaders created national interest and as a result of whispered antilabor charges against Ness, the president of the American Federation of Labor sent a personal emissary to Cleveland shortly after Donalds and McCray had been convicted to make labor's own investigation. The labor representative came to Cleveland from Washington with several assistants.

After a thorough probe, in which he was given complete co-operation by the prosecution, he declared complete satisfaction with the conduct of the case. He averred that

Ness was sincere in his efforts to clear the racketeers out of labor and affirmed that the Public Safety Director had not shown in any manner that he was antilabor or "wants to break up the unions."

Once again, Ness, whose driving ambition was to enforce law and order, was vindicated of ulterior motives.

CHAPTER 10

THE DONALDS-MC CRAY CASE HAD HARDLY FADED FROM THE headlines when Ness and his department once again were thrown into an all-out campaign—a frantic search for the "Mad Butcher of Kingsbury Run," the most elusive mass-murderer in criminal history.

This maniacal killer also was known as the "Torso Murderer" because of the manner in which he decapitated and mutilated his victims. He had been sought unsuccessfully by the Cleveland police ever since he first struck on September 23, 1935, three months before Ness took office.

The killings were so fiendish and gory that Ness absolutely refused to discuss them with his pretty wife Betty.

"They're just too gruesome to talk about," he said flatly. "They'd give you nightmares. You just forget about them."

But the murders were a never-ending source of conjecture and theory in the department, where a special detail had done nothing but search for the slayer from the moment the first two victims were found at Kingsbury Run and East Forty-fifth Street on a fall day in 1935.

The first of those two bodies was identified as that of a twenty-eight-year-old orderly at City Hospital. The other body, located nearby, was that of an unidentified man about forty years of age. Both bodies had been decapitated and savagely mutilated.

The list of victims mounted steadily.

Four months later, on January 26, 1936, the body of a forty-two-year-old woman with a vice record was found at 23-15 East Twentieth Street. The body had been hacked to pieces. The head was never located.

Six months passed and then the mad killer struck again.

On July 2, 1936, the tattooed body of a twenty-five-year-old man was discovered at Kingsbury Run and East Fifty-fifth Street. The head lay nearby, wrapped in the man's own trousers. No identification ever was made.

Twenty days later there was another macabre slaying and the newspapers began to scream for action. Good citizens, and even bad ones, were afraid to walk the streets at night. The victim this time, on July 22, 1936, was a man of about forty whose mutilated body was found at Big Creek, near Clinton Road. The head was lying nearby. Again identification was impossible.

The police worked on in grim frustration, unable to come up with a single lead. They kept doggedly at it, even when the case disappeared from the headlines. But they were getting absolutely nowhere when, less than two months later, the torso murderer claimed another victim. This sixth victim, found at Kingsbury Run and East Thirty-seventh Street on September 10, 1936, was a man about thirty years of age.

Once again the head was missing. And, as so often before, the body had been so viciously mutilated that identification was completely impossible. The newspapers took up their cry against police inefficiency but there was absolutely nothing the harried detectives in charge of the case could find. There simply weren't any clues.

Cleveland began, after five months, to hope that it had seen the last of this diabolical killer until on February 23, 1937, the mad slayer claimed another victim. Running his toll to seven, the phantom butcher left the headless torso of a young woman in a chopped-up pile on the shores of Lake Erie at the foot of East 156th Street. Once again identification was impossible.

"We can't trace a thing," detectives reported to the taut-faced Ness. "And, not knowing who she was, we can't even question her relatives or friends to get a lead of any sort."

They did identify the next victim, less than four months later, as a thirty-year-old Negro woman. Her dismembered body was found June 5, 1937, under the Lorain-Carnegie Bridge. The body was wrapped carefully in a burlap bag.

But nobody could tell detectives anything. Relatives and friends were tight-lipped. No, they didn't know anybody who might have done it. No, they didn't think the victim had had trouble with anybody.

"It isn't that they are trying to conceal anything," Ness was told. "It's just that they really don't seem to know anything. It's the damnedest thing you've ever seen."

Police still were concentrating on this latest investigation when, one month later, the butcher hacked up his ninth victim. Again the head was missing when, on July 6, 1937, the dismembered body of a man of about thirty-five was found in the Cuyahoga River at West Third Street and the Erie Railroad. Identification again was impossible.

And then after a respite of nine months, and one month after the Donalds-McCray conviction, the insane slayer claimed his tenth victim on April 8, 1938. The dismembered, headless torso of a woman of thirty was found at the foot of Superior Avenue and the Cuyahoga River.

Frustrated by his inability to crack the case, Ness summoned his "Unknowns," Manski, Davis and Virginia Allen to a session at his home.

"We've got to get this man. But frankly I just don't know how. He has great cunning and the strength of an ox."

"One thing sure," Manski interjected, "he's as coldly efficient and as relentless as an executioner when the mood comes over him to kill."

Barney Davis nodded. Virginia Allen just shivered.

"Well," Ness stated as they said good night after a long and futile discussion, "I don't know how we're going to do it, but we'll have to come up with something."

This was in mid-April and then, on August 17, 1938, the "Mad Butcher of Kingsbury Run" struck twice more to run his total of victims to twelve over a period of less than three years. Seven of them were men, five were women and in six of the cases the heads never were found.

The bodies of the two latest victims, both of whom remained unidentified were stumbled upon in a rock-filled dump on East Ninth Street near Shore Drive. One was a woman of about thirty-five and the other a man of about forty-five. Both bodies again had been dismembered.

"He's changing his technique," observed Detective Andrew Nixon, who had worked constantly on the case from the time of the first slayings. "For the first time since those first two corpses were discovered in September of 1935, he left two bodies together. There's another change from his usual tactics. This time he left the heads with the bodies."

Ness' voice was bitter.

"That's about all he has left behind. He certainly doesn't leave many, if any clues. About all we have to go on is that one of the victims we have been able to identify was a pervert and another was a prostitute. This man seems to specialize in the sort of people nobody is likely to miss."

Nixon frowned his agreement as Ness continued "the skill with which these bodies are cut up would seem to indicate some sort of surgical training. And, it would seem almost obvious, the guy has to be a psycho."

Some of the bones discarded wantonly in the last two butcherings were uncovered in a cardboard box which was traced to the area surrounding Central Market. This was a squalid section in which homeless vagabonds lived in a cluster of ramshackle huts made out of packing cases, pieces of tin and fragments of canvas and linoleum. And, Ness theorized, these impoverished residents of Shanty-town probably included many lost souls similar to those who were the mad killer's previous victims.

Shantytown would have to go, Ness declared. If he couldn't find the killer, at least he could get rid of the victims. And who was to say he might not stumble on the killer in the process?

The only way to make a clean sweep, he calculated, was to move into this fetid area during the early hours of the morning when the vagrants would most likely be at home.

Laying his plans carefully, Ness led a task force of twenty-five detectives and policemen out of Central Station on his cleanup campaign at one o'clock on the morning of August 18, 1938. They silently boarded a caravan of police cars and set out to surround the Shanty-town.

When they had all taken their assigned stations in a ring around the area, signaling that they were in position with prearranged signals from their flashlights, Ness swept a beam from a powerful flashlight across the whole tract in one wide, swinging arc—a silent order to move in. Then came the start of a mad two-hour melee which was touched off as the police scrambled, stumbled and slid down the hillside and in the darkness began to rout out the residents of the packing-crate city.

Men cursed brokenly. Mongrels howled dismally in the darkness. Cats scuttled away into the night. And Ness and his men created an ear-splitting commotion as they bashed in the doors of the shacks and, in a number of instances, had to carry out the drunken occupants. One bearded man charged out swinging a rusty shovel. Ness barely ducked in time to escape a decapitation as certain as if the shovel had been a scalpel wielded by the expert hands of the mad killer.

Thirty-five scarecrows were rounded up in all and taken to the Central Police Station in vans. There they were questioned and fingerprinted, but to no avail.

Even so, cleaning out this festering spot was regarded as something on the profit side of the ledger.

Ness did it thoroughly, too. Because that same day he ordered out the city fire department and personally supervised the operations as the firemen burned down this jungle of poverty and hopelessness.

"What do they do now?" asked Manski, who was standing on the sidelines with Ness watching the planned conflagration. "Those poor devils don't have anywhere to go now."

"I've already taken care of that," Ness replied. "I've turned these cases over to the welfare department for relocation and rehabilitation. Some of these people are perennial drifters but maybe we can help a few of them get back on their feet."

Once the "burn-out" of the Shantytown had been completed, Ness's mind again turned to the problem of the torso slayer.

"Get Barney and Virginia and we'll meet at my house tonight," he directed.

Gathering with his Unknowns in the privacy of his home, Ness explained that he was obsessed with the idea that the mad butcher must be a man who at one time had had surgical training.

"I want you three to check all of the psychiatrists in the city and see whether there are any former doctors or mental students who have been involved with schizophrenia or any other violent mental disorders," he told them. "This guy may be a nut, but he's a pretty smart one."

"From the almost professional manner in which these bodies have been dismembered, I've got to think maybe you're on the right track," Barney Davis nodded.

Ness was out of town on another matter several weeks later when Virginia Allen contacted Manski in great excitement.

"Jim," she said breathlessly, "I think I might have something on the torso killings."

"What is it?"

"Well," Virginia replied, "I didn't think it would do any harm to look around among some of my society friends. I've come up with a tip on a man named Gaylord Sundheim who comes from a very respectable family."

"Well, what about it?" Manski demanded.

The blonde Virginia's voice quavered.

"He used to be a premed student. He's a giant of a fellow and exceptionally powerful. And I learned from the family doctor that he has been seeing a psychiatrist. The psychiatrist says he definitely has paranoid tendencies and, on top of that, he is said to be a little—well, queer."

"Maybe he could fill the bill," Manski agreed.

"Maybe so," Virginia told him. "But I need help. A friend of mine tells me that Sundheim never gets home until quite late at night—and I don't hanker to go around there by myself in the dark. Just in case we are right this time."

Manski laughed and said teasingly: "You think we'd better wait until Eliot comes back to town?"

Virginia became annoyed.

"Nothing doing. I've developed this lead so far and I'm

going to follow it through tonight. But, Jim," she pleaded softly, "how about going along?"

Manski, chuckling, agreed and at ten o'clock that night they found themselves on a desolate, dead-end street where the wide lawns and high hedges looked eerie in the faint glow from one feeble street light.

"He lives in one of these two houses at the end of the street." Virginia swallowed and said in a near whisper, "Suppose you take one and I'll take the other?"

They separated and Manski disappeared behind a tall hedge as he made his way up to one house while Virginia turned and mounted the steps of the other. A light showed dimly from somewhere in the rear of the house through an opaque glass in the front door and she pulled an old-fashioned bell handle.

There wasn't a sound except for a muffled jangle from far inside and she was about to ring again when with a noiseless and disquieting abruptness the door swung open in front of her. The man hovering there, blotting out the light behind him, looked monstrous. He was big and strong all right and, she thought with rising panic, looked "nutty as a fruitcake" as he leered down at her.

"Are you Gaylord Sundheim?" she asked, trying to steady her voice.

The man ran his eyes up and down her trim figure and noisily licked his lips. His voice was surprisingly soft and ingratiating.

"I sure am, honey. What can I do for you?"

"We'd like to talk to you," she told him staunchly.

"We?"

"Yes, just a minute."

Virginia could whistle shrilly through her teeth like a man and this time she put her heart into it. Manski came on the run.

The undemonstrative Jim whistled too, but softly, as he took in the massive proportions of the man standing in the doorway.

133

"We're police officers," Manski said. "We'd like to talk to you."

The big man grinned slyly. "I got a hunch what you want."

He ogled Virginia again and smacked his flaccid lips lasciviously. Then, turning to Manski, he added, "But you haven't got a thing on me and you can talk to me when you get a warrant."

With that, he bowed mockingly to Virginia and softly closed the door in their faces.

Manski and Virginia stood there for a few moments staring at each other.

"Well," Manski observed, "he's a cool one all right. And I think maybe you have come up with something, Virginia."

Eagerly they awaited Ness' return to town the next day. And Ness, when he was filled in on what had happened, showed unusual excitement.

"He fits the pattern exactly," Ness agreed when they told him of the visit to Sundheim and the big man's calmly defiant reaction.

"It fits in with the mental picture you have drawn of the killer," Manski agreed.

Ness nodded.

"Yes, it does. Number one, he was a premed student, which would account for a certain knowledge about anatomy and dismembering a body. Second, we can believe, according to your findings, that he is a homosexual. I think we can assume, from the wayward character of one or two of the victims we have been able to identify, that they might have taken up with him. Number three, Sundheim lives in the general area and is big and strong enough to have overpowered any of them and to have been able to carry away the bodies. The diagnosis of the psychiatrist seems to be the clincher. I think we'd better pick up our Mr. Sundheim and have a chat with him."

Virginia cautioned him against any undue action.

"Remember, Eliot," she said, "he is from a well-to-do

and rather influential family. We'd better not make a mistake."

"Well," Ness said, "we won't run him in and we won't put any charges against him. But we can invite him to lunch in a hotel. And, if we happen to give him a lie detector test, it's simply a scientific 'experiment.'"

The next day Sundheim was invited to lunch. He came, after some protest, with Manski on one side of him and Davis on the other.

Ness questioned him at length concerning his activities and, in particular, where and with whom he spent his evenings. Sundheim, completely at ease, seemed to enjoy the cat-and-mouse game.

"How about taking a lie detector test?" Ness asked him as they sat alone in the hotel room. Ness had stationed Manski and Davis in the adjoining room, believing that Sundheim would talk more freely alone.

"Be sure that the connecting door is unlocked," Ness had said to his men. "This monkey is big and I don't like the look in his eyes."

Sundheim, acting as if it was all a huge joke, willingly submitted to the lie detector test—not once, but twice.

The answers came out the same way both times, the readings and replies clearly indicating that Sundheim was lying.

"I think you did those killings," Ness suddenly barked at him after studying the results of the tests.

"You think?" Sundheim laughed in his face. "Prove it. I happen to know that those lie detector tests are not admissible evidence."

Wanting to continue his examination, Ness ordered lunch sent to the room. Sundheim ordered steak and, when he finished, sat there fingering the razor-sharp steak knife and looking at Ness with what seemed to the Safety Director to be extremely calculating eyes.

Had Manski and Davis not been in the next room, Ness would have been very nervous.

Then, as Sundheim continued to fondle the blade, handling it expertly, Ness told him: "Well, that's all I guess. You can go—for now."

Sundheim chuckled, threw the steak knife down onto the middle of the table and jauntily strode out of the room.

Ness rubbed sweaty palms against the sides of his trousers as he walked over to the connecting door and threw it open.

His eyes popped as he saw that the adjoining room was empty.

He had lunched all alone with the man he was absolutely certain was the "Mad Butcher of Kingsbury Run"—and throughout that whole time the torso killer had been sitting across from him with a knife in his hand.

"Where in the hell did you guys go to?" asked the usually mild-voiced Ness, when his two aides reappeared. Manski and Davis looked at him in astonishment.

"Hell, Eliot," Manski protested, "we heard you order lunch—so we went out and had ours."

They had a nervous laugh over the incident, but then Ness turned urgently to the business at hand. He ordered a full-scale investigation into Sundheim's past and constant surveillance of the man he was positive was the torso killer.

But Sundheim outsmarted him again.

The sneering giant shortly thereafter had himself committed to a mental institution and thereby placed himself beyond the reach of the law.

Throughout the next two years, Eliot Ness and his family were cascaded with venomous, jeering postcards and letters—all scribbled in the same nearly incoherent hand. The cards always had taunting clippings from newspapers or magazines pasted to them.

"Handbook for Poisoners," said the clipping attached to one of the cards. "Legal exaction will catch up to you one day." It was signed "Your Paranoidal Nemesis."

On other cards were pasted pictures of flowers, effeminate men, and of men looking out from behind prison bars. All of them were in the same handwriting and all were posted from the same small town in which the mental institution to which Sundheim had had himself committed was located.

The nagging regularity with which the postcards and letters arrived filled Betty Ness' life with terror.

"They have a terribly evil quality," she told her husband tearfully. "Whoever is sending these must be insane."

"Don't worry about it," Eliot comforted his lovely wife. "The guy who is writing these is well out of the way and you don't have to worry about him."

His words proved to be true.

Two years later Sundheim died suddenly in the institution to which he had been committed.

The letters stopped immediately.

The case of the "Mad Butcher of Kingsbury Run" still is marked "unsolved" on the Cleveland police blotter. But Ness always was certain that Gaylord Sundheim was the man. And it cannot be denied that, once Ness forced him to seek the asylum of an institution, the slayings abruptly ceased.

CHAPTER 11

THROUGHOUT HIS INVOLVEMENT WITH THE TORSO MURDER
case, Ness did not forget the Mayfield Road Mob. Special
squads had, under his orders, kept a steady, relentless pressure on the gambling-and-vice syndicate.

Now, feeling that the torso slayer was behind bars—
even if of his own selection—Ness turned his attention
fully to these hoods.

Prostitution had always been a lucrative sideline for
the underworld. Working on the theory of his Untouchable operations during the Capone era—if you dry up
criminal profits you dry up the mobsters' income, end
their ability to pay for protection and put their backs
against the wall—Ness determined to stamp out this basic
source of income.

Early in his Cleveland career he had ordered a cleanup
along lower Scoville Avenue, once a wide-open vice district. Ness himself had led the cleanup squad in a visit to
all of the known disorderly houses and succeeded in moving
all transient girls out of the city.

Accompanied by a plain-clothes man, he had been welcomed with open arms at one house—until the heavily rouged madam found out who he was.

"You got nothing on us," she spat. "This is a decent joint."

Ness looked around at the half-dozen girls sitting around the parlor. Two of them wore filmy negligees and made no attempt to keep themselves even partially covered.

"Yes, I can see that," he said. "It's a regular finishing school for young ladies."

Then his voice turned hard. "I want to see identification from all of you."

Only the woman who had greeted him at the door could prove that the house was her legitimate residence.

"Okay," Ness snapped, "the rest of you had better be out of here—and out of the city—by this time tomorrow."

Using these tactics, Ness was able to frighten a great percentage of the transients out of town. The number of them forced to move on was enough to "hurt business" in his all-out campaign against the mob's income and it was carried on until vice dens which had flourished for years in the precinct known as the "Roaring Third" had been closed down tight.

Roaming the worst areas of the city, where many disorderly houses had been in operation, Ness located one such place in which the women were bargaining boldly from the windows with male passers-by on the street. He charged around to a side door but, before he could burst in, the women had left by a rear exit.

"They're jittery, anyhow," he commented with satisfaction. "That was a quick getaway. However, I'm pleased to find that there is so little activity now in areas where there used to be a great deal."

In spite of the relentless pressure, prostitutes still were conducting a lucrative business at certain hotels. There the traveller could get a room, bath and girl as easily as a room, bath and ice water.

Ness set out to uncover the whole operation.

He learned that vice was being run as part of the nation-wide Mafia syndicate. They would place as many as four girls in a single hotel. Within a couple of weeks these four would move on and four new ones would replace them. Tracers showed that the girls who had left would turn up in New York, Buffalo, Kansas City or elsewhere.

It was general practice for a bellhop to receive one dollar for steering a girl to a hotel-room customer. Ness persuaded certain hotel operators to promote their most trustworthy and honorable men to the position of hotel managers and to offer two dollars to bellhops who turned in an alarm instead of steering guests for one dollar.

More than three hundred arrests for prostitution were made in hotels in a little more than a year and soon the racket virtually disappeared.

Meanwhile, principally through the work of the Unknowns, the constant harassment of the gambling dens continued. Virginia Allen was the key factor here through her apparently frivolous social activities.

"There's a brand-new place which we dilettantes attended last night," she would inform Ness.

Virgina had become an expert at noting all the necessary details: exits, offices, lookouts, guards, hours in which the operators were on hand, volume of play and even the floor plan. She had a speaking acquaintance with many members of the mob and was flattered at her success when she overheard one gangster describe her to another as "one of those dumb society broads."

With her information, it was easy for Ness and his raiders to move in. The pattern was always the same. The exits were blocked off. The doors were smashed in and the raiders made a clean sweep.

Because they could not buck this undercover system

which wiped out their expensive new layouts almost as soon as they went into operation, by 1938 the harried Mayfield Road Mob had just about given up the city and had fled to suburban areas which were beyond Ness' jurisdiction.

The activity of Sidney Greenspan, who rose from lieutenant to deputy inspector under Ness, was typical of this ceaseless assault on the gambling establishments and the dedication which Ness finally had achieved in his department.

Rugged Sid Greenspan was a relentless officer. As proof, he raided one bookie, a man named Kookie Moran, a total of eighty-four times in a period of one month. Greenspan crashed in and broke up the place so often that Moran added two full-time carpenters to his staff to keep the place under repair.

It was an almost farcical byplay to the main drama. Moran was stubbornly determined to beat Greenspan and vice versa. Greenspan finally won out.

The mob, its lucrative "rentals" fading away because of increasingly unprofitable franchises, still had not given up. In an attempt to offset the police, the Mayfield Road hoodlums had set up five "nerve centers" as a replacement for the original bookie plan of individual shops. These nerve centers usually were in downtown office buildings. Each one of them had a battery of telephones to which the bookie on the street telephoned his bets, thereby lessening his chance of being apprehended with betting slips in his possession. No betting slips, no evidence for conviction.

These individual bookies thereby had become "commission men"—working for five per cent of the bets plus a percentage of the winnings without the risk of having to share in the losses. This gangland plan also reduced overhead and, in addition, kept large crowds of people from congregating in one place, a factor likely to arouse police suspicion.

But it didn't take Ness and his Unknowns long to discover the location of the "nerve centers." Barney Davis, posing as a gambler, was particularly effective.

"I've found a pip," little Barney told Ness over the telephone one afternoon. "But it's going to be difficult to nail down. It's on the seventh floor of the ——— Building and you'll have to cover the stairs, an elevator and a fire escape as well as floors above and below."

"Thanks, Barney," Ness told him. "Let's set it up for four o'clock tomorrow. You be inside in case anything goes wrong but otherwise don't reveal yourself. We'll take care of it barring any big trouble."

At four o'clock the next afternoon, plain-clothes men under Ness' direction completely bottled up this betting palace in the sky.

"There's just one trouble," one officer reported to Ness. "There's a thick steel door at the front. We'll never break through it."

"Just stand outside," Ness told him. "I'll open it from the inside."

Then, with every exit guarded, Ness climbed the outside fire escape and plunged head first through the window. Even Barney Davis, standing inside, was startled to see his chief come flying through the glass, roll to his feet, whip out a pistol and bark: "Okay, everybody hold it. This is a raid."

Keeping thirty people covered, Ness slid along the wall to the bolted steel door, released the locks, threw the door open and invited his amazed plain-clothes men to step inside.

"How the . . .?" one of them stuttered.

"Never mind that," Ness said. "Let's get these characters downstairs into the paddy wagon."

Barney Davis rode downtown with the rest of them, so as not to incur suspicion. Later in the confusion at headquarters, he simply vanished through Ness' quiet manipulation.

"Good job," Ness congratulated Davis. "We turned up bankbooks showing deposits totalling three-quarters of a million. I think the federal boys can make something out of this. The deposits are in the name of the 'Chestnut Sales Company' but a little backtracking bookwork is going to make it hot for somebody in the mob. If we can't nail them for policy extortion, maybe we can get them on an income tax evasion rap."

Ness, however, was determined to get the mob himself.

And there was a brand-new element of assistance at hand by now. The people of Cleveland knew at long last that they had a dedicated law officer at the head of their public safety department. Ness had promised to protect witnesses and he had kept his word. He had promised to send wrongdoers to jail and he had kept that promise, too. And now the people came forward to help him sound the death knell of the Mayfield Road Mob.

No less than seventy witnesses appeared, a surprising number of them voluntarily. From their sworn statements, a massive dossier was prepared against the mob. One by one, the witnesses provided full and complete details of the gang's operations across the years. Steadily and inexorably, Ness gathered his facts and figures as he prepared zealously for the final drive.

At the same time he stepped up his raiding attacks on every gambling establishment he could find, and in October of 1938 made what the newspapers hailed as the "biggest numbers haul in history."

Ness and a squad led by Detective Sergeant Mark Jackson on October 3, 1938, slammed into a private residence and arrested twelve operators, including Junius Mann and Ralph Mann, brothers of one-time "policy king" Horace Mann, who had been deposed by the mob.

When the raiders battered in the doors, they found a group of ten men and two women gathered around a large table checking the day's take on a half-dozen adding machines. The take for this one day amounted to twenty-five thousand dollars. None of those at the table was armed and they surrendered meekly, each of them obviously astonished that their hideout had been discovered. In two steel trunks, Ness and his men found several hundred thousand duplicate slips, which were confiscated, showing bets ranging from a penny to a dollar. Ness estimated from the volume of action that this one gambling spot must have used at least two hundred runners to contact bettors on the outside.

Nine of the twelve people arrested were convicted, the three others jumped bond and fled from the city.

It was another nail in the mob's coffin. And now, with a case he was sure none of the mobsters could beat, Ness was ready to make his biggest move.

On April 26, 1939, Ness threw the book at them.

On the basis of the evidence which he and his Unknowns had painstakingly compiled, the grand jury returned indictments against twenty-three members of the Mayfield Road Mob on policy extortion charges.

Headlines screamed the news. Splashed across the front pages of the newspapers were the pictures of "Big Augie" Bonelli, alias "Baby Face," fingered as the Number One man; "Little Alberto" Ruffia, the deadly, one-eyed co-dictator of "Numbers Row," and Benny Lee, king-pin muscle and trigger man.

The mob did not take it lying down.

A few hours later a flying squad of hoodlums in a black sedan raced around the city of Cleveland offering a thousand dollars in cold cash to anyone who would provide any or all of the names of the seventy secret witnesses whom Ness had not identified . . . in line with his promise to protect them from gangland revenge.

There were no takers.

The sedan later was found abandoned and was traced to Roger James, a brother of one of the twenty-three men who were indicted.

Ness had been forced to identify three of the witnesses —Francis Jones, Randolph Sellers and Michael Larue— in order to get his indictment. The wife of one of them fearfully telephoned Ness the night the five hoodlums scoured the town for witnesses and told him tearfully: "Four gunmen just broke into our house demanding to know where my husband was. They turned the house inside out before they left. The last thing they said was 'We'll be back.'"

"Don't you worry," Ness told her grimly. "From now on I'll have you under guard at all times."

The three witnesses who had been named, including the woman's husband, earlier had been spirited out of town and Ness berated himself for the delay in ordering a twenty-four-hour police watch on the families of all three.

Outraged at this flagrant attempt to intimidate witnesses, Ness relentlessly drove his department to pick up every man against whom an indictment had been returned.

"Dig into every rathole in the city," he ordered. "I want every one of these hoodlums nailed."

And nailed they were unless, as happened in several cases, they already had turned tail and run.

"Big Augie" Bonelli, white-faced and disbelieving, was brought in with his hands shackled and held in a hundred thousand dollars bail. Ness had asked for "bail so high it'll wring them dry—or leave them cooling their run-down heels in jail." He got it.

One by one they were dragged in, big and small, and most of them did "cool their run-down heels in jail."

Bonelli quickly regained his braggadocio and, protesting his innocence, boasted that "they'll never make it stick." Bonelli was merely whistling past a cemetery: he was one of the first convicted and vanned off for a two-year stretch in the Ohio State Penitentiary.

"Little Alberto" Ruffia had been one of the first to hear the news of the indictments—and one of the first to run. But Ness had planned well. "Little Alberto" was found hiding in Acapulco in 1943, returned to Cleveland and summarily convicted. "Little Alberto" was sent away on a "one-to-five" and served the full five years.

To make matters worse for him, while "Little Alberto" was in hiding, Federal Judge Stephen P. Clark had ordered his citizenship revoked and, after completing his prison sentence, "Little Alberto" was deported to his native Italy.

Long rated as Cleveland's Number One public enemy, the deadly Lee did manage to escape the extortion charges. The reason for his escape was ironic: he was sent to the penitentiary for life in the slaying of Guy Martin, an underworld figure.

One by one, the gangsters were convicted. There was no question that the Mayfield Road Mob was smashed.

And there was but small doubt that the policy racket had also been broken by the indictments and the succeeding wave of convictions or runouts.

There was an abortive attempt by some fledgling mobsters who escaped the dragnet to grab the loose ends which Ness had jerked from the mob's hands. But they lacked the "muscle" to handle the job and the operators, who once had paid tribute in the form of staggering "rental" for their franchises, scornfully refused to knuckle down to these beardless lieutenants of the indicted and fallen robber barons.

But the gambling operators soon discovered that they couldn't run without the mob either. There was no more protection of any kind in the city of Cleveland, nor the mob-supplied money necessary to wheel and deal fast enough to stay ahead of the police.

A few die-hards attempted to run their business on a limited, penny-ante scale. But the majority of them simply closed up shop because of the ever-increasing "heat" from the fair-haired young man in city hall.

CHAPTER 12

A VETERAN CITY HALL NEWSPAPER REPORTER, WHOSE BEAT included the Safety Director's office, in the "new" Cleveland of May 22, 1940, wrote a "Dear Boss" letter which his editor published in the Cleveland *Press*.

It began:

"I am wondering whatever became of Eliot Ness. I think you should know it's been more than four weeks since I've seen him . . ."

Reporters always were worried when Ness wasn't around. They knew from experience that when this happened a big story was likely to break around their heads.

This time it was no different than in the past. For on June 4, Ness turned over to Prosecutor Matthews new evidence which he had obtained from long-convicted labor racketeer Mickey Worthington providing the link between labor racketeering and the underworld.

Worthington at the time was serving, thanks to Ness, a three-to-fifteen-year sentence for blackmail on labor jobs while he was the bargaining agent for the Builders' Union.

But Eliot Ness was not finished with him yet.

As a result of the safety director's ceaseless probing, Worthington and two others were indicted on June 19, 1940, for union racketeering. The others named were Tony Sutton, president of the Builders' District Council, and Salvatore Dombrouski, who had one of the longest police records on file in the department and who already was under indictment in the million-dollar numbers racket cleanup.

The information supplied by Ness involved the trio in various bribes of from three to five thousand dollars.

Specifically, Sutton and Worthington were charged with extorting ten thousand dollars on September 20, 1936 from the Smith Nestleman Building Company of Kansas City by threatening to delay the work of those contractors. This was on the construction of a grain elevator for Northwestern Mills, Inc. They also were accused of extorting five thousand dollars from David Hearn and Giuseppe Puccini, Cleveland home builders, at the rate of a hundred dollars for each house these two men had constructed.

Sutton and Dombrouski were charged with the bombing of the Downtown Laundry Company in 1933. Sutton had one previous extortion conviction on his record: in 1918 he had received a two-year sentence on a charge of illegally obtaining two thousand dollars while he was a business agent for the Builders' Union.

Worthington, who had pleaded guilty to Ness' blackmail charges in 1937, decided to turn state's evidence because friends who had promised to fight for his parole had failed to deliver. Ness received word that he was ready to "talk business" and went to see him at the Mount Vernon, Ohio, state prison farm. He succeeded in getting the officials there to parole Worthington in his personal custody. He then established Worthington in a secret Cleveland hideout under police guard while he checked out the parolee's story.

"Sutton was the man who provided the money for me

to blow Cleveland in '37 while I was waiting trial on those blackmail charges," Worthington confessed to Ness. "He gave me five thousand dollars. Sutton told me that a delay in the trial until after a mayoralty election might mean a new mayor who would give Eliot Ness the bum's rush out of office. If that happened he said the charges would be dropped.

"There's something else," Worthington informed him. "I guess you know that a guy named Nick Teducci visited me twice at the Mount Vernon prison farm. Well, he offered me six grand to bust out of the farm and head for Mexico with my lips sealed. Now let me tell you something else. This guy Teducci is really Hal Freeman, manager of the Kleer Glass Company."

Worthington admitted that Freeman had "scared the hell out of me."

"He told me once that I'd better keep my mouth shut because he was from the mob. He told me, 'You don't want the same thing that happened to Blackman and Volte, do you?'"

Blackman was the vicious, bullying labor leader who was slain by a shotgun blast through a window of his home shortly after he had kissed his little daughter good night in May of 1936. Volte, an ex-convict and part owner of Cleveland Glass Cleaners, Inc., was killed along with his pretty girl friend, twenty-year-old Mabel Dodge, on August 4, 1939, when a bomb wrecked the car he was driving. Volte was traveling through Shaker Heights, an exclusive Cleveland suburb, when he pushed the horn on his shiny new sedan to warn another car approaching at an intersection. The pressure on the horn detonated a bomb which had been wired to it. The blast ripped off the front end of the car and killed both occupants.

Two days later an attempt was made to get Ness himself, and again it was his uncanny sense that saved him, as it had before in Chicago.

That time the Capone hoodlums had fastened a bomb

to the starter of Ness' car. They had failed, in their haste, to fasten one of the hasps which held the hood closed. Ness noticed that it was open, raised the hood and discovered the bomb.

This time it was a premonition.

"I have the strangest feeling," he told his wife Betty at breakfast. "I can't pin it down. All I can tell you is that I have a feeling something is wrong."

A deep frown furrowed his forehead but disappeared as Mrs. Ness, worried at his unusual behaviour, told him: "Do be particularly careful today, Eliot."

"Now, don't worry," he chided her. "It's probably something you fed me for breakfast."

As he left the house, the feeling persisted and then, as he slowly approached his automobile, his eyes focused steadily on it and he stopped and regarded it carefully.

"Could it be?" he mused to himself, remembering the other bombing. Feeling a bit foolish he carefully raised the hood of the car.

He was right!

There, wired to the horn, was a bomb which certainly would have put a sudden end to the career of Eliot Ness.

Gingerly he detached it and, realizing that it was harmless without electrical contact, quietly closed the hood and stuffed the bomb hastily into the glove compartment so that Betty wouldn't see it.

He would have the bomb parts traced. But he knew from past experience that it would do little good. The men who had done this were much too shrewd and expert to use any materials that might be traced.

Still, he thought as he drove away, it had been a good hunch—a lifesaving one.

Shortly after this attempt to give Ness a gangland death, Tony Sutton went on trial before Judge Philip T. Packer. It was September 26, 1940; Worthington was the chief witness.

This was the case that fully exposed the once great power of the Cleveland labor racketeers.

"We had to pay Worthington and Sutton five thousand dollars to keep carpenters on the job," testified Giuseppe Puccini, one of their extortion victims. "I didn't tell my story before because three men with guns told me I'd better keep my trap shut. But now Mr. Ness has promised that nothing can happen to me."

It was another example—as in the case of the seventy who testified against the Mayfield Road Mob—of the faith the people by now had in their Public Safety Director.

Harry Cornwall, another home builder, testified that union carpenters had been pulled off construction work on houses he was building in Lakewood and Rocky River. Cornwall said he paid five hundred dollars to Worthington, at the suggestion of Sutton, and the carpenters returned to work.

"If you pay fifty bucks a house for a seven-thousand-dollar house and one hundred a house for those over seven thousand you will be able to go ahead," Sutton told him.

Nestleman, the Kansas City construction man, revealed he had given Sutton five thousand dollars at one time and same amount to Worthington on another occasion to get pile drivers back to work in the construction of the grain elevator.

Hans F. Krantz, another in the parade of small-home builders, took the stand for the prosecution. When Worthington bled him for a payoff, Krantze grimaced: "Let's meet in the Riverside Cemetery where only the dead can be witnesses. I'm ashamed of this whole thing."

That, appropriately enough, was where the payoff was made.

"I paid tribute to Worthington too," said Louis Kennedy of Rocky River, Ohio. "But then I decided to stop."

One month later vandals broke into a house which Kennedy had nearly finished and thoroughly splattered mahogany paint throughout the interior. Three days later

Worthington telephoned and said Sutton wanted to see him. Kennedy went.

"Haven't you forgotten something?" Sutton asked. "Or do you want more trouble?"

Worthington suggested a protection payment of "three or four hundred dollars" and after some bargaining Kennedy got off by handing Worthington a hundred and fifty dollars.

"There was no more trouble," he concluded.

As a result of this revealing testimony, Sutton was convicted on four counts of extortion and sentenced to four years in the Ohio State Penitentiary. Ness had won another victory in his cleanup campaign.

The bitter end of the Worthington-Sutton-Freeman series loomed ahead when, in March of 1941, Freeman, a suave former bootlegger who once served time for a liquor violation, went on trial before a jury of farmers at Mount Vernon, Ohio, for attempting to engineer a jailbreak to spring Worthington.

One of the principal witnesses was Bernard Heinz, a respected New York businessman, who had told the grand jury that Freeman once had offered him three thousand dollars not to testify in the labor racket case involving Bob Donalds.

Getting the frightened New Yorker on an airplane to Cleveland and then by car to Mount Vernon took the combined resources of two of the era's greatest crimebusters —Ness and young Tom Dewey of New York.

Ness first went to New York to escort Heinz west for the Freeman trial; Heinz had promised he would meet Ness at an appointed rendezvous and fly back to Cleveland under his protection. Heinz never kept the appointment.

As he was leaving to meet Ness, a hard-eyed stranger stopped him in the lobby of his New York city office building, pushed him toward a phone booth, shoved him through the open door and said gruffly: "You'd better take this call."

Heinz picked up the receiver and heard a grating voice on the other end of the wire. "You'd better not testify or else—" The line went dead.

Heinz did not want to find out what the "or else" was. He simply did not meet Ness. The safety director looked for him all of that night and all of the next day but finally had to fly home alone.

Fighting against time because the Freeman trial was about to get under way, Ness telephoned an investigator in New York District Attorney Tom Dewey's office. It was he who located Heinz, persuaded him to go to Cleveland and promised that once he returned from Ness' custody in Ohio the Dewey office would give him all of the protection he needed for as long as he wanted it.

Reassured, Heinz flew west and Ness met him at the Columbus, Ohio, airport. With a heavy police guard, they drove to Mount Vernon, where at the last minute, Heinz became the key witness.

Marshall J. Adams of Mount Vernon, the foreman of the Freeman jury, said later that it was the Heinz testimony which convicted Freeman.

"Otherwise," observed the jury foreman, "it was just a question of who was the biggest liar—Worthington or Freeman."

Freeman drew a three-to-fifteen-year sentence—and Ness registered still another triumph for decency.

Even now there still was work for Eliot Ness to do.

And his next step was to wipe out the charity rackets.

Ness launched a three-month drive against Angelo Lucarno, his brother Nat, and the Universal Aid Company. They were soliciting donations in the name of reputable organizations, ostensibly to feed and clothe needy families.

"Little or none of it is going to needy persons," Ness charged. "And this outfit is taking in an estimated one hundred thousand dollars a year."

Many of the organizations whose names were used by the Lucarnos actually had charters prohibiting charity drives. Most of them swore that the Universal Aid Company merely was helping raise a few dollars to repay the cost of small booklets each organization published from time to time.

The fund-raisers worked by telephone, by mail, from a sucker list and with a group of a dozen solicitors who also picked up the money which was pledged by telephone. It was learned that many persons who had been solicited had contributed as much as one hundred dollars without checking and some had donated as much as a thousand dollars.

Ness conducted a raid on Lucarno's office and found workers operating a large switchboard. Lucarno agreed to sever all connections with the charity work but, while he took out the switchboard, Ness learned that the work was being continued by private phone and by mail.

Summoning Virginia Allen, he told her to use her society contacts to confirm the report.

"Get yourself put on the sucker list," he told her. "You might get a few of your friends to put themselves in line for some contributions, too."

Virginia worked swiftly and efficiently, gathering her information carefully and documenting it completely.

"Here," she told Ness a short time later, "are tape recordings of telephone calls made to me and some of my friends by the Universal Aid Company asking for contributions. And here—" she laid some pamphlets on his desk— "is a good cross section of their mail solicitations."

"That's great," Ness told her enthusiastically. "Now we've got them."

They did, indeed. The evidence was turned over to federal authorities because, as Ness explained, "they have a more simplified method of prosecution by nailing these leeches on mail fraud charges".

It developed just as he expected. The Lucarnos and two other officers of their company were convicted on March 6, 1940.

It was a case which also served as a perfect finale to Eliot Ness' midwest mop-up.

Peace and law at long last had come to the city of Cleveland. The filth had been sponged away.

EPILOGUE

IT WAS TOO CALM IN CLEVELAND NOW FOR BOTH NESS AND his men.

The Vandals Squad had been disbanded for a lack of anything to keep it occupied. The Unknowns had gone their respective ways without ever having revealed their identities. Edward Pierson, the assistant safety director, resigned to seek a judgeship. Mayor Burton was elected to the United States Senate.

With war blazing in Europe, Ness reorganized the Cleveland fire department and prepared it for the possibility of air raids.

Then he too resigned after six remarkably successful years as Cleveland's Public Safety Director.

Ness went on to become Federal Director of the Division of Social Protection for the Office of Defense, stamping out prostitution and venereal disease in the vicinity of military establishments and vital production areas throughout the nation. As a reward for his outstanding job in this post, he received the Navy's Meritorious Service Citation in 1946.

After the war, Ness went into private business and was so engaged when he died in 1957 at the age of fifty-four. In his relatively short lifetime, Eliot Ness deservedly had become a legend in the fight for law and decency.

JOHN GARDNER

NOBODY LIVES FOR EVER

'Take care 007. Take special care. The
Continent's a hotbed of villainy these days,
and you can never be too careful.

M's words underlined the fact that nobody
lives for ever.

A fact that James Bond, hero of LICENCE
RENEWED, FOR SPECIAL SERVICES,
ICEBREAKER and ROLE OF HONOUR would
remember again and again as his first
holiday in ages rapidly turned into the
deadliest, most ruthless game of cat-and-
mouse ever.

A game that no one found funny.

A game played for the highest stakes –
James Bond himself.

Further titles from Hodder and Stoughton Paperbacks

JOHN GARDNER

IAN FLEMING

DAVID MORRELL

BOB SHILLING

A. J. QUINNELL

All these books are available at your local bookshop or newsagent, or can be ordered direct from the publisher. Just tick the titles you want and fill in the form below.

Prices and availability subject to change without notice.

HODDER AND STOUGHTON PAPERBACKS, P.O. Box 11, Falmouth, Cornwall.

Please send cheque or postal order, and allow the following for postage and packing:

U.K. – 55p for one book, plus 22p for the second book, and 14p for each additional book ordered up to a £1.75 maximum.

B.F.P.O. and EIRE – 55p for the first book, plus 22p for the second book, and 14p per copy for the next 7 books, 8p per book thereafter.

OTHER OVERSEAS CUSTOMERS – £1.00 for the first book, plus 25p per copy for each additional book.

NAME...

ADDRESS ....

....